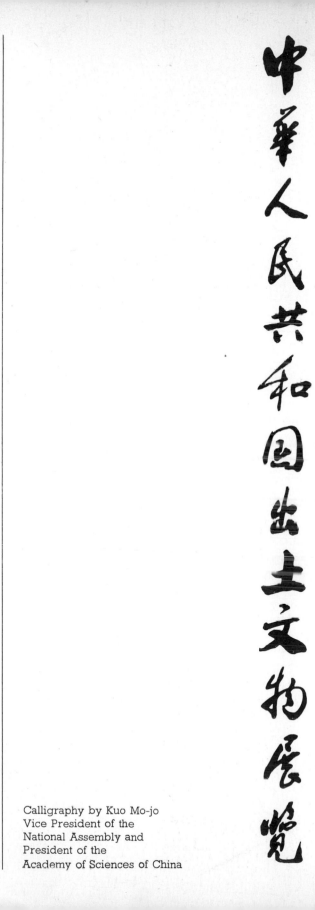

中華人民共和國出土文物展覽

An exhibition of
archaeological finds of the
People's Republic of China

Calligraphy by Kuo Mo-jo
Vice President of the
National Assembly and
President of the
Academy of Sciences of China

An exhibition of archaeological
finds of the People's Republic of China
held at the Royal Academy, London
by permission of the President
and Council from 29 September 1973
to 23 January 1974

Sponsored by The Times and
Sunday Times in association with
the Royal Academy and the
Great Britain/China Committee

The Genius
of China

First published 1973
Reprinted with revisions 1973
Text by William Watson
© Times Newspapers Ltd, 1973
All rights reserved

Designed and produced by
George Rainbird Ltd,
Marble Arch House
44 Edgware Road, London W2

Text set by Bell Press Typesetters Ltd,
London W10
Colour originated by Westerham Press Ltd,
Westerham, Kent
Printed by Westerham Press Ltd
Bound by Dorstel Press Ltd, Harlow, Essex

ISBN   0   7230   0107   3

Contents

Committees

The Chinese Committee for the Organisation of Exhibitions of Archaeological Finds

Wang Yeh-chiu
  Chairman

Hsia Nai
  Vice-Chairman
  Director of the Institute of Archaeology

Wang Chih-fan
  Deputy Secretary-General of the
  Chinese People's Association for Friendship
  with Foreign Countries

Hsiao T'e
  Ministry of Foreign Affairs

Wang Yu-tang
  Member of the Committee

Liu Kwang-ya
  Chinese People's Association for Friendship with
  Foreign Countries

Kuo Lao-wei
  Administrative Bureau of Museums &
  Archaeological Data

Wang Chen-li
  Curator

Yan Hung-liang
  Ministry of Foreign Affairs

The Chinese Exhibition Council of London

Lord Trevelyan,
  Chairman

Sir Thomas Monnington,
  President, Royal Academy of Arts

Sir Harold Thompson,
  Chairman, Great Britain/China Committee

Mr C. D. Hamilton,
  Chairman and Editor in Chief,
  Times Newspapers Limited

Mr G. S. Barrass,
  Foreign and Commonwealth Office

Mr S. C. Hutchison,
  Secretary, Royal Academy of Arts

Mr P. A. Taverner,
  for Times Newspapers, Exhibition Organiser

Professor W. Watson,
  Professor of Chinese Art and Archaeology in the
  University of London, Head of the Percival David
  Foundation of Chinese Art, School of Oriental
  and African Studies

Dr A. E. Werner
  Keeper Research Laboratory,
  The British Museum

Foreword

It was less than two years ago that news reached the West of remarkable discoveries made by Chinese archaeologists excavating ancient tombs throughout the country. This caused a sensation everywhere where the superb art of China is valued. The finds included jade suits clothing the bodies of a prince and princess of the Han Dynasty – unique objects nothing comparable to which had ever been found – and a remarkable bronze representation of a flying horse. I had the good fortune to see many of these new discoveries in Peking in January 1972.

Now these remarkable treasures which have been hidden for so long in the ancient earth of China, are in Europe and are to be shown in London. We in Britain are among the first to see them. They are all of immense interest, many are of rare quality of form and they span 600,000 years of China's past. For this great privilege we are indebted to the Government of the People's Republic of China who have generously lent us these newly found national treasures.

Our thanks are especially due to Mr Wang Yeh-chiu and his colleagues in Chinese Museums who have given most generous co-operation in making this exhibition possible. We have also to thank Mr Anthony Royle, MP, Under Secretary of State for Foreign Affairs, who first asked the Chinese Government to make this exhibition possible, and His Excellency Mr Sung Chih-kuang, Chinese Ambassador in London, and Sir John Addis, our Ambassador in Peking, who have done so much to help the arrangements.

I must record our gratitude to Times Newspapers Limited for their generous financial and administrative backing, without which this exhibition could not have taken place, and in particular to Mr C. D. Hamilton, the Chairman, for his unfailing interest and help in every aspect of the arrangements. We are also most grateful to Sir Thomas Monnington, the President of the Royal Academy, for offering the Academy's galleries to hold the exhibition, as they held another famous Chinese exhibition forty years ago.

Finally, I must record our indebtedness to all those, Chinese, French and British, who have made this a co-operative enterprise.

This remarkable exhibition is before you : we are proud to bring it to Britain.

TREVELYAN

The exhibition

Many people, companies and institutions have played their part in the extensive preparatory work for the Exhibition. It is right that such work should be acknowledged at the beginning of this official catalogue.

In the preface, Lord Trevelyan, Chairman of the Chinese Exhibition Council of London, has acknowledged the debt we owe to the people of China, their Government and, in particular the Chinese Committee for the Organisation of Exhibitions of Archaeological Finds. Their names are listed on the page facing Lord Trevelyan's preface. The Chinese Committee selected the objects on display from amongst many thousand objects, 2,000 of which were sent from provincial museums to Peking for consideration. By the time the British and French delegations arrived in Peking in February this year to discuss the details of the exhibition, the Chinese side had displayed the objects specially for us in the Museum of History. There was much useful supporting material and all had been excellently catalogued. These first-class preparations helped us greatly in staging this exhibition in London.

In London, all matters of main policy were entrusted to the Chinese Exhibition Council appointed by The Secretary of State for Foreign and Commonwealth Affairs, Sir Alec Douglas-Home. The members are listed on the same page as those of the Chinese Committee. It is right that a member of that Committee, Mr G. Barrass of the Cultural Exchange Department of the Foreign and Commonwealth Office, should be singled out for special comment. Mr Barrass led the British delegation to Peking early this year and he returned there when the exhibits were being packed. He worked long hours finalising the arrangements for the Exhibition with the Chinese Government. Mr Barrass has had the support of Mr E. V. Vines, Head of the Cultural Exchange Department, FCO and Miss J. Robertson also of that department.

At the time of writing this section of the catalogue, the exhibition of Chinese treasures now being seen in London, had just opened in Paris. We record with pleasure the close and friendly co-operation we have received from the Quai d'Orsay and the Association Française d'Action Artistique, organisers of the exhibition in France, particularly from the members of the French delegation which went to Peking with the British delegation – M. André Burgaud, Mlle Adeline Cacan and Professor Vadime Elisseeff. The latter worked closely with Professor Watson and Mr Wade in deciding on the grouping of the exhibits. He also played an important role in ensuring that the beautiful bronze flying horse (number 222) came with the other exhibits to Paris and then London.

Two executive committees under the Chairmanship of Mr P. A. Taverner (*The Times* and *Sunday Times*) have been responsible for the detailed planning of the exhibition, including its design and construction and for all matters connected with publicity and publications. The regular members of those committees were Mr P. James, Mr K. Tanner and Mr N. Usherwood (Royal Academy); Mr G. Barrass or Miss J. Robertson (FCO); Professor W. Watson (Percival David Foundation); Dr A. E. Werner (British Museum); Mr R. Wade (Designer); Mr J. Mannings (Security Adviser); Mrs J. Law and Mr E. Young (George Rainbird Limited); Miss C. Geddes, Mr B. Howell, Miss P. Kennedy, Mr G. Pearse, Mr P. Saabor and Mr J. Slatford (*The Times* and *Sunday Times*). The work of the executive committees was made easier by the constant helpfulness of all members of the staff of the Royal Academy.

The Chinese Exhibition Committee invited Mr

Robin Wade to design the exhibition. He was assisted throughout by Mrs J. Sampson, Mr R. Reed and Miss Pamela Gray whose research was indispensable. Mr Wade also advised on the graphic design. Mr Peter Hopkirk, Chief Reporter of *The Times*, performed invaluable services for the exhibition organisers, researching, writing and editing the introductory material in the galleries.

Mr G. Pearse is Exhibition Manager and Miss P. Kennedy is Deputy Manager. Miss D. Stuart-Williams is Mr Pearse's personal assistant. The exhibition management is supported by a large warding and sales staff.

The exhibits were transported from Peking to Paris where the exhibition was held from May to August by Air France and BOAC, now part of British Airways. Mr R. L. Smith, Cargo Commercial Accounts Manager, Europe for BOAC gave much care and attention to the problems raised by the long air journey from Peking. We are very grateful to him and the crews and support services who ensured that everything arrived safely in Paris.

The expert packing necessary was carried out by Chinese packers. Mr I. A. Pearson, Wingate and Johnson Limited, acted as packing consultant.

The Metropolitan Police Force and the Kent Constabulary provided an escort for the exhibits as they were transferred from Dover to the Royal Academy. We are grateful to Sir Robert Mark, Commissioner of Police of the Metropolis and Sir Dawnay Lemon, Chief Constable, Kent Constabulary for authorising the arrangements. A liaison has also been established with the Metropolitan Police to ensure that support for our own security and crowd control arrangements is available should it be needed. Throughout, the adviser on security has been Mr J. Mannings whose thorough and thoughtful work has lessened the burden which would otherwise have fallen on the exhibition management.

Dr A. E. Werner, Keeper of the Research Laboratory, The British Museum, has advised on scientific and technical matters. He travelled to Peking with the British delegation and gave much help during the negotiations there.

Special support has been given by a number of companies and in particular National Cash Register Company Limited and Jaeger.

Mrs J. Law, who travelled with the delegation to Peking, has been responsible for the preparation of this catalogue and it has been designed by Mr R. Clark of George Rainbird Ltd. The maps are by Mr J. Flower.

Mr D. Witty and Mrs C. Gascoigne, also members of the Peking party, were responsible for all the colour plates and the cover, and many of the black and white photographs, all of which are reproduced by permission of Times Newspapers. The initials DW or CG appearing after a plate number indicate which subjects each photographer took. All the other photographs are reproduced by permission of The People's Republic of China.

Finally, we would like to record our very sincere thanks to Professor William Watson for writing the text of the catalogue. His great knowledge and untiring energy have made it possible to produce it at record speed and under great pressure. This at a time when he was also helping Mr Wade on aspects of the exhibition layout and working with the BBC on major television films related to the Exhibition.

Introduction
The scope of the exhibition

This is the first exhibition held outside China in which the greater part of her cultural history is illustrated wholly by documented material, mostly from controlled excavations. Particulars of provenance and associations are known in every case. The twelve sections begin with the palaeolithic period, on which some important new evidence is available, and end in the fourteenth century AD, at a time when Europe, in the person of Marco Polo, first made direct contact with China. The masterpieces included in all the divisions of exhibits betoken the high achievement of Chinese artists and craftsmen, the anonymous spokesmen of an ancient, gifted and energetic people. They indicate also the ever-rich yield of archaeological investigation in the Chinese soil.

All of the pieces have been recovered since the establishment of the People's Republic in 1949. It is then that systematic excavation may be said to have begun, if not absolutely, certainly for the first time with adequate technique, organization and official support.

The Institute of Archaeology was founded as a branch of the Academy of Sciences in 1949. Throughout China, in the provincial capitals and other large cities, Committees for the Administration of Cultural Properties were set up to survey and control antiquities and to see to planned excavation. The Institute of Archaeology itself and the major museums have also been centres of research and education. Permanent and temporary exhibitions of art and antiquities are now a feature of Chinese life as they are elsewhere. The present exhibition offers some of the chief fruits of this work, showing China as studying and preserving the material heritage of its past in the objective and scientific spirit that our age has brought to archaeology elsewhere. The choice of pieces was in the

hands in the first place of a special committee headed by Dr Hsia Nai, Director of the Institute of Archaeology. For the selection some scores of thousands of items were assembled in Peking. It will be seen that many important groups of objects were excavated during the Great Cultural Revolution of recent years, for example, those from two rich tombs of the Han period at Man-ch'eng and Wu-wei.

China possesses no ancient buildings surviving from the remote past, such as frame the historical imagination when we view remains of ancient civilizations in the Near East and Central America. What is known of the architectural setting of pre-Han civilization is supplied only from a few representations of buildings engraved on bronze. These suffice to show that the tradition of wooden building familiar in recent and modern times traces its ancestry to the beginning of the Bronze Age in the mid 2nd millennium BC. But in the absence of buildings and monumental sculpture our imagination irresistibly clothes the ancient culture with a powerful visual character drawn from the enigmatic shapes and solemn ornament of the bronze vessels which are the most characteristic product of the pre-Han period. In the archaising art of the Sung and later dynasties their shapes and ornament were a constant inspiration to the craftsman. In this way the styles of the thirteenth–eleventh and sixth–fourth centuries BC set classic standards.

The exhibition is notably rich in examples of the early bronzes. It illustrates also daily life, the history of warfare and the progress of technology in bronze casting and ceramic glazing. From the tenth century onwards porcelains predominate among grave gifts. The study of ceramics, well established in the West since the beginning of the present century, has gained immeasurably in recent years from documented pieces like those figuring in the later sections of the exhibition. After the fourteenth century archaeological research offers less than other sources to the study of artistic and social history. The exhibition terminates at the end of the Yüan dynasty, in 1368. All but two of the twelve sections correspond to successive historical periods. The exceptions are Section Six, comprising items from the Tien kingdom which flourished during the Western Han period, and Section Nine, in which are placed textiles from Central Asia ranging in date from the first century BC to the eighth century AD, and thus spanning a number of dynasties.

The Yüan dynasty palace, Ta Tu, in Peking: a pictorial reconstruction of the residential precinct of the Hou Ying Fang.

11

Early archaeology in China

Although scientific archaeology is comparatively new to China, the study of the past in terms of material and artistic survivals is of very ancient date. Chinese antiquarianism in the pre-Han period (i.e. before about 200 BC) was much concerned with identifying the forms and purposes of bronze sacrificial vessels used in official ceremonial and in making offerings to the spirits of ancestors. Study of the traditional rites was a natural outcome of the Confucian philosophy, which saw them as sustaining the personal and political relations necessary to a stable society. This kind of antiquarianism flourished therefore between the third century BC and the second century AD, when Confucianism was first establishing itself as the orthodox world view; and again in the eleventh and twelfth centuries AD when traditional native attitudes were affirmed against the 'foreign' infection of Buddhism, in the intellectual atmosphere which produced Neo-Confucianism. Around the beginning of the Han dynasty, in the third century BC, the ancient lore of ritual vessels and symbolic jades was compiled in practical manuals. Our present knowledge of the uses of such objects, many of which survive through burial in tombs, rests largely on these writings. In 219 BC the Ch'in emperor tried to recover from a river the nine *ting* tripods on which the power of the Chou king over his feudal subordinates was said to depend. They eluded him. Later Han emperors ordered bronze vessels discovered in the empire to be presented to them, and on two occasions regnal titles were chosen to mark these events. In the revival of Confucianism eight centuries later, attention was paid mainly to inscriptions cast on the ancient bronzes, but at the same time began a more archaeological and artistic study of the vessels themselves. The *K'ao-ku-t'u* (*Pictures for the Study of Antiquity*), an illustrated work in ten volumes published in AD 1098, catalogues 211 pieces from the imperial collection, one of which was attributed to the Shang dynasty by reason of its finding at the place traditionally described as the site of the last capital of the Shang kings. This was *Yin-hsü* near Anyang in north Honan, of which more is said below. The antiquarians who wrote in China at the turn of the eleventh and twelfth centuries laid the foundations of an archaeological method which was superior in objectivity and method to the contemporary and later antiquarianism of the West.

Chronology

A scheme of early dynasties accepted by Chinese historians in the second century BC placed at the beginning two groups of three and five emperors (*San huang, Wu ti*) made up of legendary persons whose proper place is in mythology. Thereafter followed the Hsia, Shang and Chou dynasties in order, each of which was supposed to have ruled over the whole of China. When Ssŭ-ma Ch'ien wrote his history in the first century BC he decided that dates prior to a year equivalent to 841 BC were not sufficiently reliable to be worth including in his chronological table. Certain dates were later accepted as orthodox, Hsia being put between 2205 and 1765 BC, and Shang between 1765 and 1122 BC. These limits are still often quoted in modern writing. Recent scholars have however questioned the existence of a Hsia dynasty, at least as a paramount power preceding Shang, and archaeology lends it no support thus far. On the other hand the historicity of Ssŭ-ma Ch'ien's account of the Shang dynasty is corroborated by the oracle sentences engraved on bones and tortoise carapaces excavated on the site of the Shang capital ('Great Shang') at Yin-hsü. These inscriptions name most of the Shang kings listed by the historian. Modern study of fragmentary surviving texts and of lunar eclipses recorded in Shang times at Anyang point to the year 1027 BC as a more probable termination for the dynasty than the orthodox date. A recently published radiocarbon estimate supports the archaeologists' view of Yin-hsü as a late site of Shang, occupied from the fourteenth to the eleventh century BC, but cannot resolve the doubt attaching to the date of the overthrow of the dynasty by its successor, the house of Chou. Although the western calendar has now been officially adopted in China it is still customary to date the past by dynastic names. For convenience historians subdivide the long Chou dynasty (1027-221 BC) according to dates which in part are historically significant and in part arbitrary.

Immediately after the Chou conquest of central China the country was divided up into some scores of subordinate principalities which held theoretical allegiance to the king of the Chou state and were under obligation to supply him with troops on demand. A superficial comparison with medieval Europe has been the reason for calling the period between 1027 and 221 BC the feudal age of China. But the legal basis of European feudalism was totally lacking in China, and the analogy is misleading. Chinese historians have recently adopted 'feudal' in a different sense, conforming to Marxist usage, in a broad scheme of periodization. The evolutionary stage extending from the earliest appearance of man until the end of the neolithic period is designated Primitive Society. Its local self-sufficiency, communal labour free from class division and exploitation, and personal relations determined by matriarchy, are thought to be exemplified at the neolithic site of Pan-p'o. Next follows Slave-owning Society, a stage coinciding essentially with the Bronze Age, extending from the founding of the Shang dynasty to a point in the fifth century BC at which the original political dispensation of the Chou confederacy became quite ineffective. While it is debatable whether the exploitation of slaves was in the main the basis of Shang and early Chou economy, one cannot doubt the existence at that time of large numbers of slaves, who were treated as chattels. There being no clear-cut event to mark the beginning of the Period of the Warring States, the year 475 BC adopted in the exhibition is a convention (other initial dates found in current Chinese and western writing being 481, 452 and 403 BC). Thereafter, until the dismissal of the last Ch'ing dynasty by the revolution of 1912, the Chinese now term the social order feudal, as denoting arbitrary power, land-owners' privilege, the oppression of the peasantry, poor standards of justice, and, in the last few centuries, an ossifying conservatism which impeded the advance of industry and technology.

Chronological table overleaf

13

Chronological table

SECTION 1	Palaeolithic period	about 600,000 – 7000 BC
	Neolithic period	about 7000 – 1600 BC
SECTION 2	Shang dynasty	about 1600 – 1027 BC
SECTION 3	Western Chou dynasty	1027 – 771 BC
	Period of the Spring and Autumn Annals	770 – 475 BC
	Technology	16th century BC – 4th century BC
SECTION 4	Period of the Warring States	475 – 221 BC
SECTION 5	Ch'in dynasty	221 – 207 BC
	Western Han dynasty	206 BC – AD 8
SECTION 6	Kingdom of Tien	about 3rd century BC – 1st century BC
SECTION 7	Hsin dynasty (Wang Mang)	AD 9 – 23
	Eastern Han dynasty	AD 24 – 220
SECTION 8	Period of the Six dynasties	AD 220 – 580
SECTION 9	Central Asia, Han to T'ang dynasties	1st century BC – 8th century AD
SECTION 10	Sui dynasty	AD 581 – 618
	T'ang dynasty	AD 618 – 906
SECTION 11	Five dynasties	AD 907 – 960
	Sung dynasty	AD 960 – 1279
SECTION 12	Liao dynasty	AD 916 – 1125
	Chin dynasty	AD 1115 – 1234
	Yüan dynasty	AD 1271 – 1368

Historical summary

1 The palaeolithic and neolithic periods

600,000–7000 BC/7000–1600 BC

Peking Man and the newly discovered Lan-t'ien Man, living in the Middle Pleistocene, 600,000 years or more ago, are intermediate in development between the Heidelberg and Neanderthal men of Europe. Both are shown here by specimens of their stone tools and models of the skulls. The majority of pre-*sapiens* races known in China correspond to the most advanced Neanderthal type. *Homo sapiens* appears in China, as in Europe, in the Late Pleistocene, during the accumulation of the yellow earth, or loess, which covers much of the north and north-west of the country, having been deposited (according to one theory) by winds blowing from the northern periglacial zone. The flake and microlithic tools of late palaeolithic tradition persisted on the Mongolian plateau into the geological Recent period and the beginning of the neolithic period.

The neolithic cultures divide into three broad traditions. The Yang-shao culture, dating from the 5th millennium BC and economically based on millet, pig, goat and dog, has an early phase in Honan, and a later in Kansu west of the T'ao river, both occupying the primary loess and producing fine painted pottery. In Honan Yang-shao is followed by the Lung-shan culture, which is the only neolithic found east of Honan to the coast. Its black polished pottery, the finest product, is notable for skilled throwing. The Ch'ing-lien-kang culture, in the region around the Yangtze mouth, belonged to cultivators of wet rice. Its polished stone tools are particularly varied and well formed.

2 The Shang dynasty

1600–1027 BC

The Shang state, centred on Honan, the first historical principality in China, represents also the earliest phase of bronze-using culture in East Asia. From about the sixteenth century BC Shang kings ruled at a walled city near modern Chengchou, and about 1400 BC moved north of the Yellow river to a new capital at Anyang, which was occupied until the defeat of Shang by the Chou confederacy of west China. The date of this event was 1122 BC according to the traditional dynasty table, but 1027 BC as revised by modern scholars. Constantly warring, en-

The neolithic village at Pan-p'o, Shensi, in the course of excavation.

The site at Lan-t'ien where the bones of Lan-t'ien Man were discovered in 1966.

The floor of a bronze foundry at Cheng-chou, Honan. Shang dynasty.

slaving enemies who might be slaughtered in royal tombs, the Shang kings ruled a slave-owning theocracy, consulting an oracle on practical and ritual affairs by inscribing and burning animal shoulder bones and tortoise carapaces. To appease ancestors' spirits they used superb, strangely decorated and strangely shaped bronze vessels in rites of animal and human sacrifice. Recent excavations reveal the variety of Shang art and the surpassing skill of the bronze casters. Finds made in Shansi, Anhui and particularly Hunan give important new evidence of the extent of Shang rule and culture.

3 The Western Chou dynasty and the Period of the Spring and Autumn Annals
1027–771 BC/770–475 BC

After King Wu of Chou had defeated the Shang, the Chou kings continued to rule from ancestral territory, their capital Hao-ching being situated a short distance south-west of modern Sian. In 771 BC King P'ing built a new capital just west of the present site of Loyang. Under the Chou feudal organization a ceremonial of sacrifice resembling the Shang institution was continued, but now took on an im-

The royal tomb at Wu-kuan-ts un, Anyang, Honan. Shang dynasty.

portant political and social rôle, the vessels frequently being inscribed with a text commemorating an award by the king or by the ruler of a subordinate principality to a deserving officer, who then cast the bronze in question. In this period the official decorative art shows intensive and inventive development of consecrated ancient themes, accompanying designs of provincial origin.

The Period of the Spring and Autumn Annals was a time of increasingly difficult relations between the principalities and the central kingdom of Chou, the influence of whose official art declined. A new and complicated movement appears in the ornament of bronze and heralds the dominant artistic trend of the following centuries. Towards the end of this period lived Confucius, now the best known and in his lifetime one of the least successful of a class of men who argued social and moral philosophy, and attempted to influence rulers and to gain office. He is said to have edited the historical work after which this period is named. At this time bells used in ceremonial music are frequently deposited in great tombs.

4 The Period of the Warring States
475–221 BC

The name is justified by the incessant warfare of the principalities now owning to merely ceremonial acceptance of, or wholly disowning, the authority of the Chou kings. Ch'u in the south and Ch'in in the west eventually stand out as the main contenders. It is a period of rapid advance in iron metallurgy, and in bronze casting by the lost wax method (the mould being formed around a wax model, which is then melted away). Forms of land ownership, the military *corvée*, the rising power of merchants and political professionalism are social phenomena which laid the foundation of traditional Chinese society and earn the name of feudal currently given to it by Chinese historians. In this turbulent age philosophy flourished, specu-

The grave goods as excavated in a tomb of the Western Chou period at T'un-hsi, Anhui.

lative or moral-political, notably in the persons of Chuang Tzŭ and Confucius' disciple Mencius. In bronze art the miniaturist schemes of the so-called Huai style, and the adoption of inlay with precious metal are remarkable. Jade carving is revived and refined. Some of the most striking of these works come from the tombs of princes of the Ch'u state.

5 The Ch'in and Western Han dynasties
221 BC–AD 8

The first Emperor of Ch'in, Shih Huang Ti, united China after long internecine warfare, completed the frontier of the Great Wall on the north, proscribed Confucians and burnt their books, standardized weights and measures and instituted an intensely practical and despotic regime. Little in writing or art can be attributed closely to Ch'in time, but under the following Western Han dynasty a revival of the arts matches an intellectual renaissance. Bronze craft, lacquer, jade, painting, sculpture all reflect the change and much of these arts is demonstrated by the contents of the great tombs of Prince Liu Sheng and his wife at Man-ch'eng in Hopei. Horizons had suddenly widened through Wu Ti's campaigns in Central Asia, which took Chinese arms as far as Sogdiana, between the Oxus and the Jaxartes. The tall, 'celestial' horses which were introduced thence into China symbolized the marvels of the far west. External and internal trade expanded and enriched a new class. Confucianism flourished in office. The wealth of an established nobility may be judged from the Man-ch'eng tombs.

6 The Kingdom of Tien in Yünnan
3rd–1st century BC

In Yünnan around the Tien lake a small kingdom of semi-nomadic cattle-raisers believed that their

The earth foundation of a tiered building in the precinct of Lin-tzŭ, Shantung, the capital of the state of Ch'i. Period of the Warring States.

rulers descended from a scion of the house of Ch'u. In 109 BC their king accepted the suzerainty of the Emperor Wu Ti of China and was awarded the gold seal and purple ribbon of a tolerated petty monarch. The contents of tombs at Shih-chai-shan, near Kunming, the necropolis of Tien kings, include articles of purely metropolitan Chinese workmanship with others which incorporate local tradition in striking original works. The exhibits are taken from the latter group. The modelling of animals and representation of village scenes are unprecedented in China, the product of an art that vanished after the full annexation of the Tien territory in the 80s of the first century BC.

7 The Eastern Han dynasty
AD 24–220

The Eastern, or later, Han dynasty is separated from the Western Han by the interregnum of the Emperor Wang Mang (AD 9–23), who for his own ends energetically supported Confucianism and the educated élite of literati, enacted a land reform

The tomb of the prince Liu Sheng at Man-ch'eng, Hopei, during investigation.

The stone gateway to the inner chamber of the tomb of the princess Tou Wan at Man-ch'eng, Hopei. Western Han dynasty.

ostensibly in the peasants' interest, and made state monopolies of wine, salt, iron, and the exploitation of mountains and lakes. Under the emperors of the restored house of Han a reaction to Wang Mang's reforms gradually established a class of landowners of even greater wealth and influence than their predecessors. Officials came from their ranks, or vied with them: the tomb at Wu-wei in Kansu and the famous tombs with pictorial reliefs in Shantung, typify the wealth and ostentation of these men. From Wang Mang's time, and by his example, Taoist beliefs and magical practices spread among the educated, but Confucianism was still unshaken as the official code. The Eastern Han capital was moved from Ch'ang-an (Sian) to Loyang in Honan. In the late first century AD we see the Chinese hold on Central Asia threatened but retained; in the second century the struggle of landowners finally resolved into the rivalry of three great parties. Eunuchs' intrigues at the palace and the popular movement of the Yellow Turbans contributed to the weakening of central government. Politically the country was ready to fall apart, but economic prosperity grew steadily, and in the arts the triumph of realism and experiment over the traditional formalism amounted to a revolution. Western Han belonged to the old Chinese world, but Eastern Han, in art as in many institutions, is at the beginning of what in the eyes of the outside world has become the more familiar tradition of Chinese civilization.

8 The Period of the Six dynasties
AD 220–580

After the fall of the Eastern Han, China was not united again until the establishment of Sui rule in AD 581. A tripartite division existed between AD 220 and 265, and further splintering occurred in the fourth century. Thereafter a more settled division justifies the term 'Period of the Northern and Southern Dynasties'. In the north the alien Toba (Turkic) house of Northern Wei ruled all the Yellow river valley and eventually reached far into Central Asia. In the south the southern Ch'i state kept the Yangtze. Before the Sui unification further fragmentation had occurred, but the contrast of north and south persisted. In art as in philosophy the greatest event was the introduction of Buddhism, which brought western themes, but only initially introduced close imitation of western style. Soon, particularly in the southern state of Liang and in Northern Ch'i, Buddhist sculpture expressed Chinese aesthetic values. During the Six dynasties, again in the south, the foundations of the Chinese tradition of painting as we know it today were laid, in an atmosphere of keen aesthetic and technical enquiry. No less important was the achievement of the potters of Kiangsu and Chekiang in the third to the fifth centuries, for they advanced ceramic technique to the point from which the late-T'ang and Sung porcelains began their great cycle of invention.

The group of bronze horsemen and carriages found in the tomb at Wu-wei, Kansu. Eastern Han dynasty.

9 Textiles of the Han period to the T'ang period and manuscripts and food from the T'ang period

Archaeologically the extent of Chinese authority and trade in Central Asia – through the basin of the Tarim from Tun Huang at the exit from China proper to the Pamir plateau – is traced by finds of textiles. Fortunately the dry sandy soil of the burials in which they were found has often preserved fragments of the weaves in good condition, their colours little affected by twelve or twenty centuries underground. The Silk Route along which the trade passed followed the north edge of the Tibetan massif (the K'un-lun mountains) or the southern foothills of the T'ien-shan, passing through the chief oasis cities. The trade was at its height in the Han period, and again in the T'ang period, but in the interval, when Chinese contacts in Central Asia were broken or weakened, the caravans still went through. The main Chinese export was silk, which for many centuries China alone could produce and weave. From the sixth century AD the Roman and Iranian west possessed the secret, but Chinese silks remained supreme. The sophistication of Chinese weaving technique, from the Han period onward, is manifest in twills and damasks. The decoration of the weaves eloquently witnesses

Foundations of houses excavated at Turfan, Sinkiang. T'ang dynasty.

The excavated foundations of the Han-yüan Palace, Sian, Shensi. T'ang dynasty.

to the interchange of artistic ideas between east and west. The acceptance by China of elements of Iranian design holds a special interest.

10 The Sui and T'ang dynasties
AD 581–906

After a rapid unification of the country, the Sui emperors were still engaged in much internal war. Their rule lasted from AD 581 to 618. To their great credit they yet had time and money to spend on canal works which completed the network of China's waterways, so essential for economic welfare and for the success of central government. Notable advances in sculpture and pottery can be attributed to the Sui period, but the movement in the arts in which the Chinese style blossomed as never before and which spread Chinese taste from Japan to Turkestan was reserved for the T'ang, to which, in art as in politics, Sui is a prelude. The high T'ang style was formed towards the end of the seventh century, and centred on the capital at Ch'ang-an, near the modern city of Sian. At home peace and prosperity seemed secure, and throughout Central Asia Chinese authority was more firmly entrenched than at any time previously. Intensive trade with western countries along the Silk Route brought to China exotic goods and ideas, and in art stimulated the imitation and adaptation of Iranian themes. Silk stuffs, silver and polychrome pottery, chiefly produced at Ch'ang-an, tell the same story, reflecting the polished, luxurious and cosmopolitan life of one of the greatest capitals in

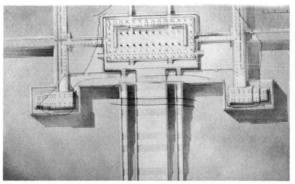

The plan of the Han-yüan Palace as excavated (within the hatched line) and reconstructed, at Sian, Shensi. T'ang dynasty.

A pictorial reconstruction in elevation of the Han-yüan Palace, at Sian, Shensi. T'ang dynasty.

the world. In retrospect we endow this floruit of T'ang with a poignancy it did not feel: in 756 An Lu-shan's rebellion broke out, the emperor fled from Ch'ang-an, and the colourful life of the capital suddenly ended. Fifteen years later the political situation was restored, but the liberal cosmopolitanism and splendour of the old culture were not recaptured. Textiles, silver, and lead-glazed three-colour pottery in the exhibition are eloquent of cultured life. They speak no less of the skills which made Chinese craftsmen the wonder and envy of the world.

11 The Period of the Five dynasties and the Sung dynasty
AD 907–1279

In the history of art the period of the Five Dynasties is remarkable for its great painters, whose work made possible the achievements of the masters of the eleventh and twelfth centuries. Upon reunification in 960 by General Chao K'uang-yin, who became the first Sung emperor, the north-east beyond the wall remained in the hands of the Khitan confederation of Turkish and Mongol tribes, who named their dynasty Liao. The early Sung emperors, manipulating finance to meet the cost of large armies and of the tax evasion by great land-owners, were faced with an unprecedented inflation. Cultural affairs reflect little of the imminence of military and economic collapse. In contrast to the T'ang period, when Buddhist philosophy and other external influences affected much of Chinese civilization, the Sung dynasty is a time of intense nationalism, when the intellectual and artistic values of tradition were reasserted, newly fructified and expanded. More than ever one notes the rôle of the

The foundation deposit of a pagoda in Ting-hsien, Hopei, in the condition in which it was discovered. Sung dynasty.

court in establishing and propagating standards in art and craftsmanship. Under Hui Tsung (1101–1126) a painting academy was organized and the influence of this imperial aesthete-collector was supreme. Works from his own brush survive. In 1127 the Chin Tartars overran north China, establishing their own dynasty; and the Sung court withdrew from K'ai-feng in Honan to a new capital at Hangchow south of the Yangtze mouth. The art of this Southern Sung period, as seen in painting, has a withdrawn and contemplative romanticism contrasting with the bolder constructions of earlier Sung painters. The material recovered in archaeological excavations does not include paintings, but much of the strength of the Northern Sung style, and the sophistication of the Southern Sung connoisseur, introspective and archaizing, is embodied in porcelains. In the Southern Sung period the best of these were made under palace control, and have long been regarded as the crowning achievement of ceramic art.

12 The Liao, Chin and Yüan dynasties
AD 916–1368

The Liao dynasty established by the Khitans of north-east China, with territory mostly beyond the Great Wall, lasted through the whole of the Five dynasties and the Northern Sung dynasty, from 916 to 1125. Between 1115 and 1234, while Sung emperors still ruled the south from Hangchow, the north was under the Chin dynasty. The Mongols, whose emperors called their house Yüan (original), had completed their conquest of China by 1271. Their rule lasted only eighty-eight years, until 1368, Kublai being followed on the throne by grandsons. The Mongols attempted simultaneously a despotic control of their Chinese subjects and a personal assimilation of Chinese culture. Many Chinese intellectuals and artists out of patriotism eschewed the advantages of the summons to court, but the greatest of the painters, Chao Meng-fu, had no qualms in rallying to Kublai. No baleful effect upon art can be attributed to the foreign rule. Painting flourished. Ceramics, in China always a sensitive barometer of informed and less informed taste, has something to tell. The austerities and careful archaism of the Southern Sung cease, and pleasure is taken increasingly in pictorial decoration and some exuberant ornament, which in the first place perhaps appealed to the nomads' court, In particular the great and promising innovation of underglaze painting with cobalt blue was introduced, of which some of the finest examples attributed to the Yüan period are included in the exhibition.

China in the East Asian context

The pre-Han influence exerted by China on neighbouring cultures was intermittent, depending on the borrowing of some Chinese ideas in bronze technology and art. The socketed axe of the Shang period and animal motifs on bronze harness pieces of Western Chou are examples of these. But from the Han dynasty we witness a more general expansion of Chinese culture into the surrounding areas. In the first place this was into regions of China itself which had not previously been taken fully into the Chinese sphere. Soon after the Chou settlement at the end of the eleventh century BC the territory of the middle Yangtze valley is found under the rule of the Ch'u state, which proceeded to extend its control north-eastwards into Anhui. Ch'u culture, although distinct, was closely related to that of the metropolitan area of the Wei and Yellow river valleys. Its influence reached beyond the Nan-shan to the south coast before the Ch'in unification of 221 BC. The sinicization of the south was more effective when at the end of the second century BC the emperor Wu Ti of Han conquered the Nan Yüeh, a powerful federation of peoples inhabiting the southern seaboard, and a full measure of Chinese civilization was implanted in their territory. The farthest advance was into Annam, the modern North Vietnam.

The situation which arose when Han civilization was not totally assimilated may be ideally studied in the material excavated from the necropolis of the nobles of the Tien kingdom of Yünnan, which is so well represented in the exhibition. Meanwhile Chinese influence was spreading also to the northeast. In part the Han acculturation was an inevitable process, artistic ideas following in the wake of armament and technology. The bronze and iron metallurgy of north China began to enter Korea from the late third century BC. This movement was felt at once across the sea in Japan, where it stimulated the rise of the rice-growing Yayoi culture. But Chinese civilization was disseminated in the north-east no less from military colonies founded in Korea, of which the chief was at Lolang, where examples of Han art have been excavated in abundance, particularly fine lacquers. The East Asian expansion coincided with the establishment of Chinese control in the oasis cities of Central Asia as far as the borders of Iran.

Thus at the end of the Han dynasty a political structure had been created whereby Chinese influence spread in varying degree through the whole of Central and East Asia, from the marches of Burma to Japan, along the Tarim basin from the Oxus to the Amur mouth. After the fall of the Eastern Han dynasty in AD 220 China was divided into small kingdoms until 581, but channels of communication pioneered politically and exploited commercially remained open. Similarly in later times, when Khitan Turks confined the Sung emperors to the south of their country, political division had little effect on the basic cultural unity.

In ancient Chinese theory only one independent legitimate power is recognized, that of the Chinese emperor, to whom all nations on earth owe submission, whether they acknowledge it or not. In East Asia Chinese institutions were copied and perpetuated by neighbours eager to share in the great civilization. The king of Tien with his claim to descent from a Chinese ruling house is a small example of the cultural satellite. Japan, from the sixth to the eighth century engaged in the wholesale import of Chinese technique, art, social usages, tastes and religion, is the greatest. Korea owed no less to China in founding her civilized life. In the sphere of art the cultural unity of East Asia is symbolized by the wooden building style, the superlative tradition of practical and artistic pottery, the painting style, and by a host of minor crafts, all of which stem from China. In the realm of language, literature and philosophy the same claim can be made. What Egypt, Greece and Rome have been to the West, China has been to the East.

Reference to publication of the exhibits

WW *Wen-wu* (Cultural materials)
KK *K'ao-ku* (Archaeology)
KP *K'ao-ku hsüeh-pao* (Archaeological Journal)
PP *Ku-chi-ch'ui tung-wu ho ku-jen-lei* (Vertebrate and Human Palaeontology)
PPR *Hsi-an Pan-p'o* (Report on excavations at Pan-p'o)
AD *Wen-hua ta-ko-ming ch'i-chien ch'u-t'u wen-wu* (Archaeological Discovery during the Great Cultural Revolution), 1972
HR *Historical Relics of New China,* 1972
SR *Ssǔ-ch'ou chih lu* (The Silk Road), 1972
Roman numerals refer to plates.
PPR references may indicate only a similar specimen.
Where no reference is given the piece is published here for the first time.

Item	
1	PP 10 (1966) i. VI, 5
	PP 8 (1964) 1. II, IV
	HR 4
3	PP 10 (1966) 1, 31. f 2. II
4	PP 10 (1966) 1, 30, f.1. I
5	HR 5
6	PP I (1959) 4. I, II
7-10	HR f. 7
11-13	HR f. 8
14	PPR CXV.
	HR 21
15	PPR CXIX, 4
	HR 22
16	PPR CXI, 2
17	PPR CXXXI
18	PPR CXXIV, 1
19	PPR CXXX-CXXIII
20	PPR CXVII
21	PPR 161-162, cf. CLI
22	PPR CIX, 3
	HR 20
23	PPR 59-60, LXIII-LXIV
24	PPR 72-75, LXVIII, 9-21

Item	
25	PPR LXVII-LXCIII
26	PPR LCIV-LCV
27	PPR LCVI
28	PPR LCIII
	HR 11 (middle)
29	PPR LC-LCII
30	PPR CI, 30-33
31	PPR C, 1-24
32	PPR CXXXIX
34	KP 1960.2.14. I,4
35	*Ibid.* I,6
36	*Ibid.* I,9
37	*Ibid.*
38	WW 1972.3.77. f.2
41	KP.1964.2. I.2
42	KP.1958.1. IV
43	KP.1959.1.16. V,6
	HR 15
45	KP.1958.1. IV,8
	HR 14
46-49	KK.1963.4.209
50	KP.1958.1. XVI,3
51	*Ibid.* XVI, 2
52	KK.1963.7.348. III,8
53	*Ibid.* 349. II,6
	HR 29

Item	
54	KK *Ibid.* II,4
	HR 31
55	KK *Ibid.*
56	KK.1963.7.348. I, 2
	HR 33
57	KK *ibid.* I,1
	HR 34
58	KK *ibid.*
61-62	*Erh-li-kang* 34. XXV,3-4
65	*Ibid.* XXVI, 3-9
66	*Ibid.* 34
67	KP.1957.1.63. V,4
68	Erh-li-kang 35. XXVI, 11-16
70	WW.1955.10.31. XII
71	WW *ibid.* 29. VII
	KP 1957.71. III,2
72	WW *ibid.* IV
	KP *ibid.* III,6
73	WW *ibid.* 30,38.f.13 ; *ibid.* IV,i
76	KK.1965.10.502. f.2,16. III,4
77	Ehr-li-kang 21.III,2. f.4,2
79	WW.1960.10.57,59. f.1,2
	HR 48
80	WW.1959.1.Inside cover pl.
	HR 49
81	WW.1958.1.36. Cover pl.
82	WW.1960.7.50.f.5
	HR 46
83	HR 43
85	KP 5 (1951).34.XVI,1, 2
87	HR 39
88,89	KK.1972.2.4.f.6,5
90	KK.1963.8.414.f.2,3. II.4
91	KK.1963.8.415.II,6
92	*Ibid.* 414.f.4.II,1
93	*Ibid.* f.2,2.II,3
94	*Fu-feng Ch'i-chia-ts'un ch'ing-t'ung-ch'i ch'un* 7.f.4
95	*Ibid.* f.2
96	WW 1955.8.16.IV
97	WW 1965.6.52.f.2
98	HR 55
99	KP 59.4.75.f.10, 5-7.IV
100	KK 1963.5.238.III,V
101	*Ibid.* III,3
102-110	*Shou-hsien Ts'ai-hou mu ch'u-tu yi-wu.* 10. XXI (top right),LII-LXIX
111	KK 1964.10.498.f.1.I,

Item	
1-2	HR 66
112	KK 1965.10.502.f.2.6. III,2
113	*Ibid.* IV,7
	HR 38
114	KP 5 (1951).34.XVI,2
115	WW 1955.8.27.VIII
116 ;117	WW 1965.6.52.f.1
119	WW 1956.1.32.f.1.X, 1,2
120	W. Watson *Archaeology in China* pl.28
122, 123	WW 1960.8/9. 7.f.3
124	WW 1972.5.14.V,3
	HR 75
125	HR 72
126	WW 1958.9.17
127	WW 1955.8.43.f.4
128	WW 1966.5.33
129	WW 1965.36.I
130	HR 77
131	WW 1966.5.36.f.20
132	KP 1965.1.V,1
136	WW 1964.9.55.f.1,2
137	HR 80
139	KK 1972.1.15.III,1
	AD 29 (upper)
	HR 96
140	KK 1972.1.III,2
	AD 29
	HR 96
141, 142	KK 1972 1.III,2
	AD 29
	HR 96
143-148	KK *ibid.* 13
149	*Ibid.* 17
150,151	AD 21
154	AD 15
155	AD 4
157	AD 14 (lower)
158	KK 1972.1.13
161	AD 16 (lower)
162,163	AD 16 (upper)
164	KK 1972.1.11.VI,4
165	*Ibid.* 11
166	*Ibid.* 10,11
167	*Ibid.* 11.VI,2
168	KK 1966.4.7.II,1,2
169	WW 1963.11.5/6.f. 6-10. III,1.2.
171,172	WW 1966.3.2.I
	HR 93
174	HR 86
175	WW 1963.11.5.f.4-6. I,II
176	KP 1956.1.53.f.12.IV
177	*Shih-chai-shan fa-chüeh pao-kao* 106 XCVI.2

Select bibliography

L. Ashton and B. Gray, *Chinese Art* London 1935

J. Ayers, *The Seligman Collection of Oriental Art* London 1964

Cheng Tê-k-'un, *Archaeology in China* vols I-III Cambridge 1959-63

H. G. Creel, *The Birth of China* London 1936

W. Eberhard, *A History of China* London 1950

M. Feddersen, *Chinese Decorative Art* London 1961

C. P. Fitzgerald, *China: A Short Cultural History* London 1961 (paperback 1965)

B. Gray, *Early Chinese Pottery and Porcelain* London 1953

S. H. Hansford, *Chinese Carved Jades* London 1968

W. B. Honey, *The Ceramic Art of China and other Countries of the Far East* London 1945

R. S. Jenyns and W. Watson, *Chinese Art, The Minor Arts* I, II Fribourg 1963

S. E. Lee and W-K Ho, *Chinese Art under the Mongols: The Yüan Dynasty* Cleveland 1968

M. Loewe, *Everyday Life in Early Imperial China* London 1968

M. Medley, *A Handbook of Chinese Art for Collectors and Students* London 1964

M. Medley, *Yüan Porcelain and Stoneware* London in press

J. Needham, *Science and Civilization in China* vols I-IV London 1945-72

Oriental Ceramic Society, *The Ceramic Art of China* London 1972

L. Sickman and A. Soper, *The Art and Architecture of China* London 1956

M. Sullivan, *Introduction to Chinese Art* London 1961

W. Watson, *China before the Han Dynasty* London 1961

W. Watson, *Early Civilization in China* London 1966

W. Watson, *Ancient Chinese Bronzes* London 1962

W. Watson, *Cultural Frontiers in Ancient East Asia* Edinburgh 1971

W. Willetts, *Chinese Art* London 1958

W. Willetts, *Foundations of Chinese Art*, London 1965

J. Wirgin, *Sung Ceramic Designs* Stockholm 1970

P. Yetts, *The Cull Chinese Bronzes* London 1939

Colour plates

35

41

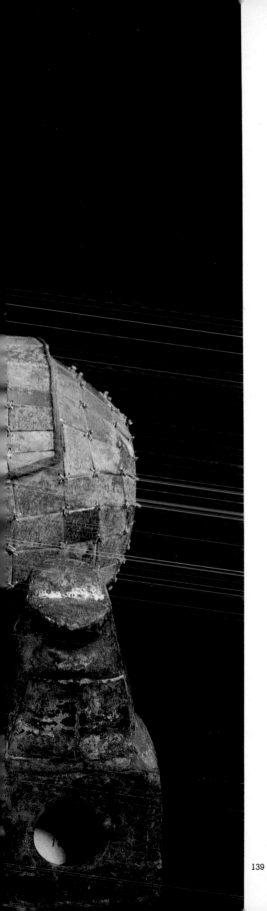

98

93

139

206,207
222

251

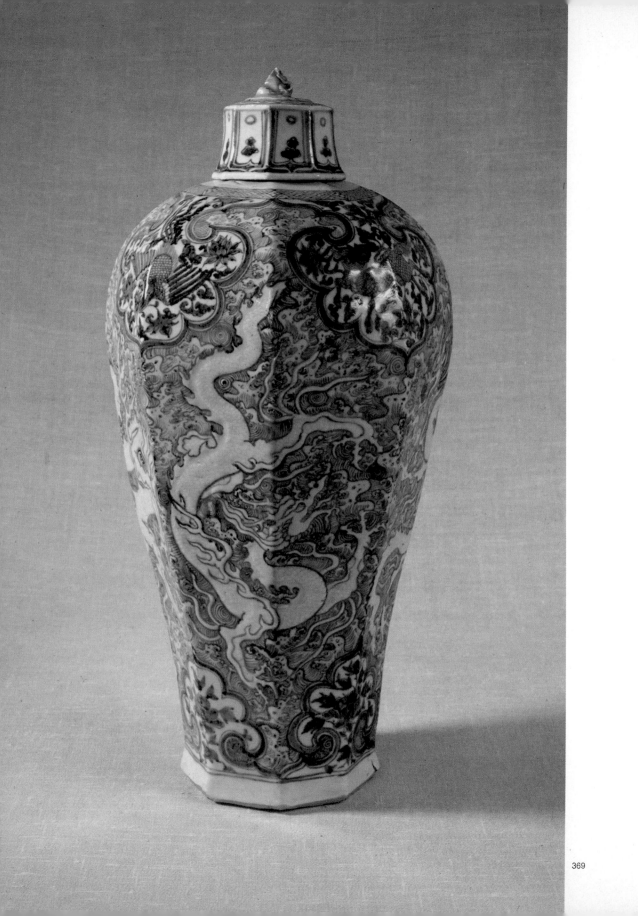

369

The exhibits

Entries in *italics* denote
documentary exhibits

Palaeolithic period
600,000-7000 BC

Neolithic period
7000-1600 BC

新石器时代 旧石器时代

Stages of human evolution from the most primitive forms are represented in China. In Yunnan in 1956 teeth of a pre-hominid ape were found with bones of mastodon, and assigned to the Lower Pliocene. Jaws of a large ape, *gigantopithecus*, also related to the pre-hominids, found in Kwangsi, belong to the Lower Pleistocene, of about a million years ago. The earliest human type is Lan-t'ien man, *Sinanthropus lantienensis*, identified from a jaw found in 1963 and part of a skull found in 1964, near together in reddish clay at Lan-t'ien, forty five kilometres from Sian in Shensi. The morphology of the bones suggests an evolutionary stage just prior to *Sinanthropus pekinensis*, and comparable to that of the *Pithecanthropus robustus* from East Java; but Lan-t'ien man's tools are little inferior to those of Peking Man. The latter is better known, being represented by complete skulls and long bones discovered in excavations at the limestone caves of Chou-k'ou-tien, forty kilometres south-west of Peking. The specimens found in 1929 and lost during the late war are now replaced by a cranium and jaw excavated respectively in 1966 and 1959. The skull of Peking Man has a capacity about two-thirds of the modern average, his heavy eyebrow ridge depressing the upper rim of the eye sockets into an irregular line. The broad nose, high cheek-bones and a shovel-shaped depression on the inner face of his incisors are features seen in the modern population of Mongolia and northern China.

The importance of the Chou-k'ou-tien discovery lay in its close association of skeletal remains with evidence of the essentially human activities of tool-making and fire-making, and in this respect the site is still unique for the evolutionary stage it represents. The tools broadly resemble those of the Acheulian culture of Europe (the most apparent dissimilarity being the effect of the intractable

1,2

2,3

5,6

11-13

8-10

material, as compared with flint, that Peking Man was obliged to use) and divide into choppers and pointed hand-axes made from bulky fragments or from large flakes, and small scrapers made from smaller flakes. It seems that Peking Man did not much resort to splitting pebbles in the manner of some other regions of palaeolithic culture in Asia.

From the lowest to the highest position in the Chou-k'ou-tien caves where Peking Man's remains were found no change in his physical character is perceptible, through a period of several hundred thousand years, beginning about 500,000 BC, corresponding to the Middle Pleistocene. He disappears before the onset of the climatic conditions attending the deposition of the blanket of loess soil which covers much of north-west China. Other human types known from remains found in Kuantung, Hupei and Mongolia, of the Middle and initial Late Pleistocene, are physically in advance of the more primitive representatives of the European and West-Asian Neanderthal man, but are still not to be classed as modern man, *Homo sapiens*. The latter appears together with stone tools classed as upper palaeolithic at the so-called Upper Cave at Chou-k'ou-tien, which he occupied *during* the formation of the loess, in the Late Pleistocene. In this race and other contemporary early types are to be seen features suggesting them to be the ancestors of all the main branches of humanity inhabiting East Asia at the present day.

Archaeological research has not yet demonstrated a clear cultural sequence intermediate between upper palaeolithic, with its stone blades and arrowheads, and the developed neolithic culture, so well documented in the valleys of the Yellow river and its mid-way tributary the Wei, which is named after the site of Yang-shao in Honan. Pan-p'o, the site from which exhibits are drawn to represent the Yang-shao neolithic culture of central China, belongs to an advanced stage of neolithic farming economy and society. The excavation in 1954-7 of a large part of it was a landmark in the investigation of the Neolithic of East Asia as a whole. Smaller sites, with simpler equipment, fewer houses and less sign of social organization may be earlier, illustrating an initial stage of the Yellow river neolithic, but this cannot yet be satisfactorily demonstrated archaeologically, by stratigraphy. It is possible that the remains of early neolithic culture are buried below deep river gravels, or were long ago destroyed by erosion as the river wandered widely and raised its bed in the valley.

The farmers of Yang-shao culture often lived in large villages (Pan-p'o village housed 200-300 people) near water, grew millet as a staple, and raised pigs, goats and dogs. The self-fertilizing and water-holding properties of the loess were to their advantage, but access to water might be difficult and particular skill in providing water through the dry months, and even for simple irrigation, is to be presumed. The village of Pan-p'o was divided into three areas, for habitation, the manufacture of pottery and burial. Group burial was frequent, and is argued to indicate a matriarchal social structure. In kilns of comparatively advanced design, capable of temperatures up to about 1000°C., the villagers made a red-surfaced pottery in simple rounded shapes, sometimes painting on it ornament which may in some instances have had overt symbolic meaning. Hunting and fishing were still important sources of the food supply, and stone and bone tools were made in rudimentary traditional shapes. Cloth of fibre was produced in straight weave, and basketwork in herringbone pattern.

As one leaves the generative centre of neolithic culture in Honan and south Shensi, and enters Kansu, a sudden break in pottery styles is to be observed on the north-south line of the eastern edge of the T'ao river valley. West of this line, on the upper waters of the Yellow river, pottery with painted ornament of an elaborate and sophisticated kind is found in burials. There is less sign of large settlements, but the neolithic population was still dense. The designs are chiefly scrolled and geometric, but occasionally the figure of an animal appears. Previous suggestions that this Kansu Yang-shao culture was the earlier, being an offshoot of the widespread painted pottery tradition of the Iranian plateau and inner Asia, are now disproved, for it has in recent years been clearly shown to be later in date than the Yang-shao culture of Honan, and to be directly antecedent to other Kansu groups of painted pottery (Hsin-tien and Ssŭ-wa cultures) which reach well into the bronze age. The Kansu painted urns are among the most beautiful ever produced in like cultural contexts.

In neolithic China one thus sees scant but sufficient evidence of an aesthetic tied to magical notions and significant ornament, of a kind familiar in the art of modern primitives. The human faces and fish of Yang-shao designs are probably to be considered in this light, as more explicitly magical-auspicious than the themes of the later Yang-shao tradition of Kansu, although these too retain a vague symbolism.

Meanwhile the central Yang-shao of Honan was replaced by another neolithic culture having strong affinities with the east coast and the north-west. This is the Lung-shan culture, denoted archaeologically by its distinct black-surfaced and burnished pottery, of which thin-walled vessels displaying ingenious employment of the fast-turning potter's wheel are characteristic. In Honan the

14-32

14-16

23-32

21-22

33-36

37

52-58

53-55

Lung-shan (so-called from the type-site of Ch'eng-tzu-yai in Shantung, near to the Lung-shan – 'Dragon Mountains') is found at places stratified *over* the Yang-shao and *under* remains of the Shang period, its intermediate position in the cultural succession of this nuclear region being thus manifest. The most advanced form of Lung-shan culture is found at sites in East China (Ch'eng-tzu-yai, Jih-chao, Wei-fang, all in Shantung) and, in relative isolation, in the region of the Yangtze delta (Liang-chu). Two theories are propounded on the origin of the Lung-shan cultural tradition: that it is simply the later stage of a unitary development which took place in Shensi and Honan, being evolved from the Yang-shao without external stimulus (the view now accepted in China); and that it represents the rise to predominance of cultural traditions whose origins are rooted in the east, particularly in Shantung, and which have immemorial connexions leading north-eastwards into eastern Siberia (as exemplified by stone rings). It is important to note that some quite peculiar Lung-shan features, such as the elaborate use of white clay to produce original pottery shapes like the *k'uei*, are confined to the eastern zone.

The tradition of painted pottery also had a sequel east of Honan. This is seen in the Ch'ing-lien-kang culture of Kiangsu, whose elegant product is well represented in the exhibition. Lung-shan and Ch'ing-lien-kang shared the same tradition of stone tools, which is distinct from that of Yang-shao. Thin, squared axes with an exact perforation for hafting are characteristic of the earlier region. The stone knife is a tool used, it is thought, in harvesting crops and cutting other vegetation, which was common to the whole neolithic realm north of the Yangtze, the better shaped examples belonging to the eastern part. The segmented axe is peculiar to the Yangtze valley and the south. Both the Lung-shan and the Ch'ing-lien kang farmers favoured sites on low mounds on the river plain, and both depended on rice as staple, combined with the yield of the hunter and fisherman. The terrain lying between Shantung and Honan, the lower fluviatile deposits of the Yellow river, probably first saw human occupation when Lung-shan farmers penetrated into it. Previously it had not existed, being the result of the gradual advance of the Yellow river delta, or had been impenetrable to man.

50

56-58

38-41

42,45

43
44

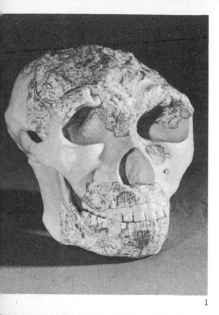

1

Casts of the skull and lower jaw-bone of Lan-t'ien Ape-Man found in excavations at Lan-t'ien, Shensi, in 1963 and 1964.

Height 18 cm
Middle Pleistocene

2

Model attempting to portray the living head of Lan-t'ien Ape-Man.

Height 43.2 cm

The inclined position of the head is assumed from the like features of Peking Man, where it is vouched for by the formation of the skull base.

3

Cast of a pointed quartzite tool made by Lan-t'ien Man, as found in excavations at Lan-t'ien, Shensi, in 1965.

Length 17.5 cm
Middle Pleistocene

The tool is formed of a long flake skilfully struck from a prepared core. The technique is in advance of that employed in the Acheulian culture of Europe, but apparently less skilled than that of the European Middle Palaeolithic.

4

Cast of a quartz scraper made by Lan-t'ien Man, as found in excavations at Lan-t'ien, Shensi, in 1965.

Length 2.8 cm
Middle Pleistocene

The shapes of the tools are little diversified, this scraper being less clearly adapted to its purpose than the corresponding tools of Peking Man.

5

Cast of the skull-cap of Peking Man excavated at Chou-k'ou-tien in 1966.

Height 11.9 cm
Middle Pleistocene

The projection of the brow-ridge is greater than that seen in many specimens of Neanderthal Man, and comparable to that of the more primitive Pithecanthropus skull found in central Java.

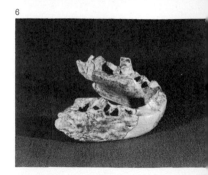

6

Cast of the lower jaw-bone of Peking Man as excavated at Chou-k'ou-tien in 1959.

Height 3.9 cm
Middle Pleistocene

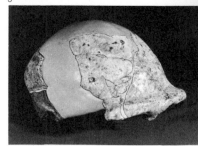

7

Hammer-stone used by Peking Man found in excavations at Chou-k'ou-tien in 1966.

Length 8.2 cm
Middle Pleistocene

This tool is likely to have served to strike stone flakes in the manufacture of other tools, and suggests that this work was done in the inhabited cave.

8,9

Flint scrapers found in the excavations at Chou-k'ou-tien in 1966.

Length 13.2 cm, 8.6 cm
Middle Pleistocene

10

Quartz scraper found in the excavations at Chou-k'ou-tien in 1966.

Length 4.5 cm
Middle Pleistocene

This scraper and numbers 8 and 9 are simple flakes or chance fragments which served all the purposes of a knife in working wood and in skinning and dismembering animals. The majority of Peking Man's tools found at Chou-k'ou-tien bear marks of usage, but very few show signs of secondary working in their manufacture.

11,12,13

Burnt earth, bone and stone from the habitation of Peking Man, found in the excavations at Chou-k'ou-tien in 1966.

Length 24 cm, 11 cm, 8.5 cm
Middle Pleistocene

Such evidence of continuous life in the cave gives the site of Chou-k'ou-tien a special interest, suggesting a stable community with an assured local supply of food.

14

Shallow red pottery bowl with everted rim, painted in black with a stylized face, excavated in 1954–7 at Pan-p'o, Shensi.

Height 17 cm, diameter 44.5 cm
5th–4th millennium BC

The circular mask recurs on another bowl with two fish attached to the head, as if whispering in its ears, and in both instances the design is associated with another of a fish. The latter is here reduced to a four-tailed rhombus, but other examples are more realistic. If the figure has totemic significance, it must be connected with the fish catch, and serve a magic purpose similar to various other schematized designs of fish which were painted on the bowls. It is notable that the convention of the face painted on this bowl shows no relation to the *t'ao-t'ieh*, an evil-averting monster mask which pervades the later bronze-age art of central China (see number 74).

Bowls with everted rims curiously painted are known both in the Yang-shao of central China and in the later Kansu Yang-shao, but the latter often add elaborate linear ornament to the interior, whereas the earlier bowls are mostly left plain.

15

Deep bowl of red pottery painted in black with a band of triangles and parallel lines, excavated in 1954–7 at Pan-p'o, Shensi.

Height 9 cm, diameter 15.5 cm
5th–4th millennium BC

15

16

Deep bowl of red pottery with contracted mouth, painted in black with triangles and parallel lines, excavated in 1954–7 at Pan-p'o, Shensi.

Height 12.7 cm
5th–4th millennium BC

The pigment used in decorating Yang-shao bowls (see also numbers 15 and 20) was generally applied directly on the burnished clay surface. Instances occur in which the painting is executed over a slip of white clay, a technique which thus appears for the first time in ceramic history. Some Yang-shao vessels, generally superior ones, have potters' marks scratched into the surface, but these are hardly of a complexity or individuality to suggest the direct antecedents of the Chinese ideographic script.

16

17

17

Pottery vase with pricked surface, excavated in 1954–7 at Pan-p'o, Shensi.

Height 11 cm
5th–4th millennium BC

This piece represents the simplest, bag-shaped vessel of the Yellow river Neolithic, such as survived until the bronze age. The pricking is in part decorative, and in part intended to improve firing by allowing the heat to penetrate better into the clay.

18

Pottery vase covered with finger-nail impressions, excavated in 1954–7 at Pan-p'o, Shensi.

Height 15 cm
5th–4th millennium BC

The narrow base is characteristic of Yang-shao bowls of superior make.

18

19

Red pottery amphora with pointed base, excavated in 1954–7 at Pan-p'o, Shensi.

Height 43 cm
5th–4th millennium BC

This type of vessel is confined to Shensi, being unknown farther east on the Yang-shao sites of Honan. The surface is generally covered with the impressions of twisted or whipped cords which were wound around a paddle and used to beat out the form against a stone pressed on the inner surface. The tapering upper part would be made separately and luted to the lower body before firing. Slung by strings from the handles, the amphora could be filled by lowering into a stream from a height, an advantage in Yang-shao country where loess banks tended to be high and vertical.

19

20

20

Shallow red pottery bowl with everted rim, painted in black with stylized deer, excavated in 1954-7 at Pan-p'o, Shensi.

Height 17 cm, diameter 42.8 cm
5th–4th millennium BC

A few birds and deer, extremely simplified, are the only animals the potter painted besides fish. They may have the same magic intent as the drawings of fish (see number 14) for in the Yang-shao economy hunting came second to fishing as a supplement to food crops and animal raising.

21

21

Red pottery bowl excavated in 1954–7 at Pan-p'o, Shensi.

Height 10.5 cm, diameter 24 cm
5th–4th millennium BC

The base is marked with the impression of basketwork apparently made of bamboo strips. The mat on which

22

23

the pot was placed allowed it to be turned for rounding the lip.

22

Red pottery bowl excavated in 1954–7 at Pan-p'o, Shensi.

Height 4 cm, diameter 13 cm
5th–4th millennium BC

The base is marked with the impression of a coarse straight-woven fabric of hemp or similar fibres which probably was used also to allow turning, like the basket-work of number 21.

23

Polished stone axe excavated in 1964-7 at Pan-p'o, Shensi.

Length 12 cm
5th–4th millennium BC

The sub-cylindrical axe of oval section is the hallmark of the Yang-shao neolithic, being found principally on the middle and upper courses of the Yellow river and in central China as far as the Yangtze. The sides and butt are often left rough or only partly polished, and generally taper from the cutting edge or have a slightly waisted outline. It is presumed that the axe was fixed in a perforation or lashed in a fork at the end of its haft.

24

24

Polished stone chisel excavated in 1954-7 at Pan-p'o, Shensi.

Length 8 cm
5th–4th millennium BC

25

25

Polished stone adze excavated in 1954-7 at Pan-p'o, Shensi.

Length 6 cm
5th–4th millennium BC

Elongated tools, of carefully squared cross-section are a notable feature of the Yang-shao, intended for comparatively refined woodworking. The adze has the cutting edge ground off-centre, or wholly at one side of the tool, while chisels like number 24 are edged symmetrically.

26

Bone spatula excavated in 1954–7 at Pan-p'o, Shensi.

Length 11 cm
5th–4th millennium BC

Such tools were made from the large bones of cattle. scraped and polished, or more rarely, from deer antler, The intention was to make as flat a blade as possible, perhaps to be used in planting or shovelling. Some

26

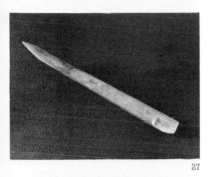

27

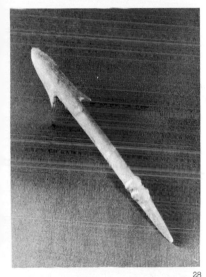

28

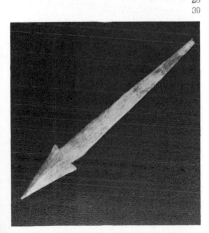

28
30

specimens show a notch in the edge near the butt which would firm the lashing to a haft.

27

Bone chisel excavated in 1954-7 at Pan-p'o, Shensi.

Length 14 cm
5th–4th millennium BC

The use to which bone chisels might be put is obscure; possibly they were tools of the potter, or served to work leather or even to shape the angles of domestic structures – seats, recesses, ovens, convenient surfaces – which the Pan-p'o villagers were accustomed to carve in the virgin loess of their hut floors.

28

Bone harpoon head excavated in 1954–7 at Pan-p'o Shensi.

Length 13.8 cm
5th–4th millennium BC

29

Bone arrowhead or **harpoon head** excavated in 1954–7 at Pan-p'o, Shensi.

Length 6.1 cm
5th–4th millennium BC

The reason for the location of Yang-shao villages near the banks of streams just above the floodplain of the main river was no doubt suitability for fishing no less than the availability of water for agriculture. The bone harpoon head number 28 is most likely to have been used on a harpoon for attacking fish, and the points generally interpreted as arrowheads might have served the same purpose. Compare numbers 47, 48.

30

Bone hairpin excavated in 1954–7 at Pan-p'o Shensi.

Length 16 cm
5th–4th millennium BC

Long hairpins of bone or metal have been used in China from the earliest time. The taper of some neolithic specimens and their sharpening at both ends suggests that they might also serve as awls in making garments from skins or coarse cloth.

31

Bone needle excavated in 1954–7 at Pan-p'o, Shensi.

Length 16.5 cm
5th–4th millennium BC

Bone needles of all sizes down to a few centimetres were found in the excavations at the village, testifying to comparative refinement in making thread and sewing clothes.

30

31

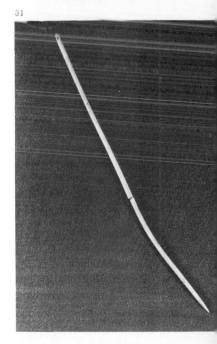

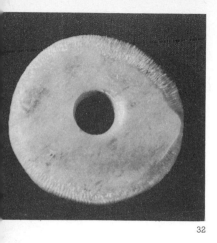

32

32

Stone spindle-whorl excavated in 1954–7 at Pan-p'o, Shensi.

Diameter 3.8 cm
5th–4th millennium BC

The evidence for weaving at Pan-p'o is seen directly in the textile impressions which sometimes appear on the base of pottery vessels (compare number 18), and is vouched for by needles and spindle-whorls. From the herringbone pattern of basketry impressed on pottery we may surmise that the weaver also had taken a first step towards elaborating her work by twilled weaves.

33

Red pottery bowl with linear ornament on the inside, excavated in 1966 at Lan-chou, Kansu.

Height 9.5 cm, diameter 23 cm
Late 3rd millennium BC

This is the Kansu equivalent of the Pan-p'o bowls described at numbers 14 and 20. The Kansu version is decorated on the inside with circles, segments of circles and triangles.

34

Red pottery tazza *tou*, with undulating ornament painted in black, excavated in 1958 at Lan-chou, Kansu.

Height 16.4 cm
Late 3rd millennium BC

35

Red pottery vase with contracted waist and black-painted ornament of bands, reticulation and rosettes, excavated in 1958 at Lan-chou, Kansu.

Height 18.3 cm
Late 3rd millennium BC

The gloss of the paint results from the burnishing of the leather-hard clay before firing. Each rosette is formed of nine rondels painted in white pigment. The deeper red beneath the painting suggests a preliminary wash with diluted clay containing haematite (red oxide).

Colour plate.

36

Funeral urn of red pottery painted with striped circles in black and brown, excavated in 1956 at Yung-ching, Kansu.

Height 49 cm
Late 3rd millennium BC

Vases of light red clay, burnt almost to stoneware hardness, are the most striking achievement of the Chinese neolithic potter. The pigments of the brush-painted ornament consist of haematite and black iron oxide containing some manganese. Inevitably symbolic

33

34

36

meanings have been read into the great variety of scrolled pattern these urns present, but whatever meaning of this kind may remotely attach to them, the designs are mainly aesthetic in intent. In the belief that the lines of dog-tooth fringeing the main lines of the design were confined to pottery placed in graves this motif was formerly designated 'death pattern', but it has now been found also on pottery recovered from habitation sites.

37

Red pottery amphora decorated with a footed snake painted in black, excavated in 1958 at Kan-ku, Kansu.

Height 38 cm
Late 3rd millennium BC

This appears to be the earliest representation of the dragon of Chinese myth. In later times it is described as amphibious and benevolent, but sight of the whole animal being dangerous to man, it is represented partly hidden in cloud or water.

37

38

Pottery bowl with incurving rim painted with scrolled ornament in red and white, excavated in 1966 in P'ei-hsien, Kiangsu.

Height 10 cm, diameter 18 cm
Late 4th or 3rd millennium BC

East of Honan neolithic painted pottery is rare, and chiefly represented by some remarkable vessels of the Ch'ing lien-kang culture of Kiangsu. These are decorated with scrolled and curvilinear figures derived from the style of Shensi and Honan, and copy the occasional practice of the Honan potter in using a coat of white clay (a 'slip') as a ground for the painting. Low bowls poised on a small

38

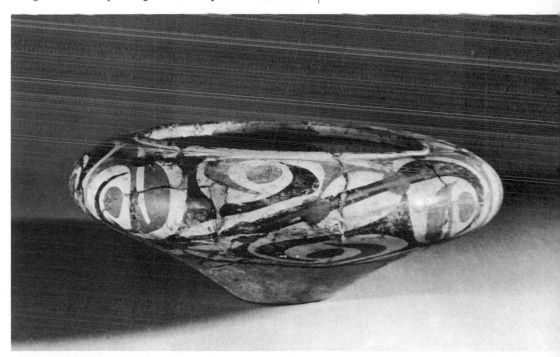

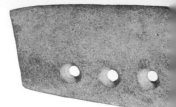

foot achieve the acme of elegance to be found in the neolithic hand-made ceramic.

39

39

Spherical pottery vase painted with a petal design in red and white, excavated in 1966 in P'ei-hsien, Kiangsu.

Height 19.5 cm
Late 4th or 3rd millennium BC

The ornament is a simplified version of the less regularly intersecting circles of the Honan tradition, and by that token appears to be a later product than the painted pottery of the Yang-shao culture. The shape is exceptional among the neolithic vessels.

40

40

Pottery bowl with everted rim, painted with rhomboids in ovals, in black and dark red over a white slip, excavated in 1966 in P'ei-hsien, Kiangsu.

Height 16.5 cm, diameter 30.2 cm
Late 4th or 3rd millennium BC

The shape of the vessel and the painting of the rim conform to the Yang-shao usage of Honan.

41

41 (DW)

Deep pottery bowl with everted rim, decorated with eight-pointed stars in white on a light red ground, excavated in 1963 in P'ei-hsien, Kiangsu.

Height 18.5 cm, diameter 33.8 cm
Late 4th or 3rd millennium BC

The ornament marks the decline of the decorative tradition initiated in the Yang-shao culture, the rich red of the older painting giving way to an eccentric pink, and the movement of the earlier design of intersecting circles and curvilinear triangles yielding to a less imaginative static scheme.

Colour plate.

42

Polished stone axe with perforation, excavated in 1956 at Nanking, Kiangsu.

Length 15 cm
Late 4th or 3rd millennium BC

The eastern tradition of stone axes differs from that characteristic of Yang-shao culture (compare number 23). In the Ch'ing-lien-kang and Lung-shan cultures the axes are flat and comparatively thin, oblong or trapezoid in outline, with a perforation towards the butt. The perforation is parallel-sided, apparently made by a drill of bamboo armed with abrasive. The trapezoid axes are more or less closely associated with the Lung-shan culture of the eastern seaboard, whereas the oblong axes spread farther inland. The rounding of the form seen in the Ch'ing-lien-kang specimen is characteristic of the realm of that culture on the lower Yangtze.

42

43

43

Polished stone knife with seven hafting holes, excavated in 1956 at Nanking, Kiangsu.

Length 22.6 cm
Late 4th or 3rd millennium BC

Stone knives used in cutting crops and other vegetables are a feature of all the neolithic cultures of north and central China, and in some parts survived late enough to be imitated in iron.

44

44

Segmented axe of polished stone, excavated in Wu-hsien, Kiangsu.

Length 17.3 cm
Late 4th or 3rd millennium BC

The segmented axe belongs properly to south and south-east China beyond the Yangtze valley, its northernmost distribution reaching to the region of the Yangtze mouth and of the Ch'ing-lien-kang culture. It therefore relates chiefly to southern neolithic culture in which hunting predominated over food production and where rice was the main crop.

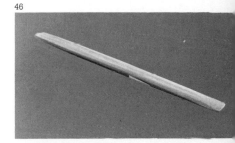

46

47

45

Polished stone hoe excavated in 1955 at Nanking, Kiangsu.

Length 13.5 cm
Late 4th or 3rd millennium BC

The breadth of the cutting edge as compared with the height of the tool makes it likely that it was used for breaking earth rather than cutting wood.

48

46–49

Bone chisel, fish-spear, arrowhead and needle excavated in 1960 at Wu-chiang, Kiangsu.

Length 16.3 cm, 16.5 cm, 16 cm, 18.1 cm
Late 4th or 3rd millennium BC

Compare numbers 26–28, 29, 31.

45

50

Penannular ring *chüeh*, of white jade (nephrite), excavated in 1956 at Nanking, Kiangsu.

Diameter 6.2 cm
Late 4th or 3rd millennium BC

Rings of white and green jade are found in tombs of the Ch'ing-lien-kang and Lung-shan cultures, and their manufacture and cult use continued into the Shang period. Similar rings were made in the Baikal region of Siberia, which is likely to have been the source of jade reaching China. The symbolic meaning of the rings and penannular rings can only be guessed at. In later times

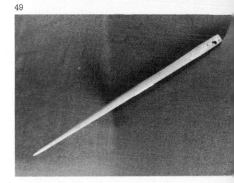

49

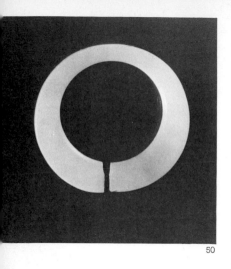

50

the jade ring in the form of *pi* (compare numbers 226 and 227) was taken as a symbol of the sky and was prescribed by ritualists as the instrument of royal sacrifice to Heaven. The technique of working nephrite by long treatment with powdered abrasive was not confined to China, being known in cruder form also in Baikalia and in the Urals at an equally early time. The question of the possible occurrence of nephrite in China has been much debated, some place-names suggesting a source in Honan or Shansi, but none is recorded to have been found there. A far trade in jade from Siberia in antiquity precedes the no less distant trade with Khotan in western Central Asia which has supplied jade to China from medieval times to the present.

51

Half-ring *huang*, of green jade (nephrite), excavated in 1955 at Nanking, Kiangsu.

Length 12.6 cm
Late 4th or 3rd millennium BC

51

The half-ring makes rare appearances in neolithic graves, and was later consecrated in bronze-age ritual tradition. According to the ritual manuals compiled in the third century BC, the *huang* was one of the Six Instruments used in sacrifice to Heaven, Earth and the Four Quarters, the 'dark *huang*' being appropriated to the North. While there is no reason to think that the symbolism of ritual jades was so strictly prescribed in the neolithic period or even in the Shang period, it appears that the later tradition drew on very ancient beliefs attaching to the rare material and to the laboriously worked shapes it was given.

52

Tripod bowl *ting*, of burnished black pottery, excavated in 1960 at Wei-fang, Shantung.

Height 15 cm
3rd or early 2nd millennium BC

52

53

The *ting* is the hallmark of the Neolithic of the middle course of the Yellow river, and it survives to appear in both pottery and bronze during the Shang and Chou periods. Under the Shang dynasty and later the noble metal tripod had august association with ritual, royal award and solemn burial, but the pottery version was still a utilitarian vessel, as no doubt it had been in neolithic times. The tripod is a particular product of Honan potters: in the Yang-shao period it makes a first, rare and eccentric appearance, and is commonest in Shang. It passes to the Ch'ing-lien-kang neolithic culture at the mouth of the Yangtze, but in typical form it is rare in eastern Lung-shan. Thus the *ting* appears to be instituted as a regular type in Honan and to pass gradually eastwards, so supporting to some extent the argument that the Lung-shan culture as a whole developed on a basis of Yang-shao culture in Honan, rather than taking its rise as an independent east-China tradition in which occasional elements were absorbed from farther west.

53

Beaker with two ring-handles of burnished black pottery, excavated in 1960 at Wei-fang, Shantung.

Height 12.5 cm
3rd or early 2nd millennium BC

Much of the Lung-shan neolithic pottery is black, either in the entire fabric or with a black surface on a grey core, but only a minority of it displays the polished surface which in the finest specimens recalls the Attic ware of Greece. Analysis of the surface shows only a higher concentration of carbon as compared with the body, and there has been much debate how the lustre was achieved. Part at least of the process seems to have been the damping of the kiln flame at a point which induced the surface of the clay to absorb particles of carbon, the surface of the leather-hard clay having been burnished before firing. Lung-shan black pottery was fired in an enclosed chamber which allowed sufficient control of ventilation to ensure a reducing atmosphere.

54

54

Tall beaker _tou_, of burnished black pottery, excavated in 1960 at Wei-fang, Shantung.

Height 16.1 cm
3rd or early 2nd millennium BC

A tazza consisting of a fairly deep bowl on a tall foot is a pottery form made in the Yang-shao Neolithic of Kansu, and, on a lower foot, in the Shang period (when it appears also made of white kaolinic clay). Subsequently it can be traced through the early Chou period made in bronze and lacquer as well as pottery, and from about 500 BC becomes one of the commonest shapes of the funerary ware. This _tou_ is not found in the neolithic cultures of central China, in Yang-shao or in the variety of Lung-shan which followed it. It is however, made in a version peculiar to the eastern zone of Lung-shan, usually as a mere cup on top of a tall tubular foot which is little inferior in diameter. In the present instance the cup has been almost eliminated as a distinct part of the design. The sides of the vessel are very thin, and the whole is an example of the virtuoso throwing characteristic of the later phase of Lung-shan. Pieces of this quality are almost invariably burnished and deep black.

55

Dish on a high foot _p'an_, of burnished black pottery, excavated in 1960 at Wei-fang, Shantung.

Height 18.7 cm, diameter 43.8 cm
3rd or early 2nd millennium BC

The pottery _p'an_ of Lung-shan anticipates the bronze type cast under the Shang and Western Chou dynasties, destined for ceremonial washing. Among Shang bronzes it is comparatively rare, and probably belongs to the end of the dynasty. In the burnished black pottery of Lung-shan the _p'an_ appears as a variant of the _tou_ tazza. The profile of low basin and stout foot resembles some Shang pieces made of white kaolinic clay and decorated with carved designs.

55

56

Red pottery tripod jug *k'uei*, excavated in 1960 at Wei-fang, Shantung.

Height 31.8 cm
3rd or early 2nd millennium BC

57

White pottery tripod jug *k'uei*, excavated in 1960 at Wei-fang, Shantung.

Height 29.7 cm
3rd or early 2nd millennium BC

The *k'uei* is peculiar to the eastern zone of the region of Lung-shan neolithic culture, being chiefly confined to Shantung province. In this piece the body is divided into three lobes descending to the legs in the manner of the *li* vase which is characteristic of Lung-shan culture in its western extension into Honan. Other specimens, such as number 56, have the solid legs of the *ting* tripod. In each case these forms strictly denote the Lung-shan culture and period, for they are not found on Yang-shao sites, the earlier tripod vessels being of a distinct kind. The *k'uei* owes nothing to the fast wheel which was introduced to China by the Lung-shan potter, but it shares with the wheel-turned pottery a taste for elaborate structure unusual in early ceramic art. Both in these pots and in those thrown on the wheel there is a suggestion that the shape and details of metal vessels are imitated. In the present instance the applied pellets of clay and the ridge at the shoulder might be thought to reproduce the like features of vases made of sheets of bronze rivetted together. But no trace of metal working has been found in excavations on Lung-shan sites, and the shapes of the bronze vessels of the succeeding Shang dynasty do not match the Lung-shan shapes very closely.

58

White pottery jug *ho*, excavated in 1964 at Wei-fang, Shantung.

Height 31 cm
3rd or early 2nd millennium BC

This jug is classified apart from the *k'uei*, numbers 56 and 57, because of the lid and spout, although it is similar, and like them representative of the eastern zone of Lung-shan culture. The *ho* belongs also to the range of bronze vessels made under the Shang and Western Chou dynasties for the libation rite (compare number 91), often in eccentric shapes. The light clay of this piece and the preceding *k'uei*, commonly used by the Lung-shan potter for superior pieces, appears to be an impure kaolin. The same whitish clay sometimes formed the floor of Lung-shan dwellings.

56

58

57 (D°

Shang dynasty
1600-1027 BC

The remains of the Shang period are illustrated in the exhibition from excavations in Honan conducted from 1950 (Anyang) and from 1959 (Cheng-chou), the results of which added decisively to those of the earlier campaigns at Anyang (1929-36).

For an archaeologist the greatest problem in the Shang period is the explanation of the apparently sudden rise of highly skilled bronze metallurgy. One of the earliest bronzes known is such a piece as the *li* from Cheng-chou (75) which in terms of the Western technical evolution might be classed with the Late Bronze Age or the Classical era, although in China it seems to have had no more elementary antecedents, and to mark an initial stage of bronze-age culture. For many technical and historical reasons the attempt to explain the Chinese phenomenon through a cultural transfer or influence from some Western Asiatic civilization proved to be illusory. In the future an earlier stage of Chinese bronze technique may be discovered (however unlikely this appears to be on the present evidence) but thus far it has eluded the investigators. By its virtual theocratic rule, walled cities, richly furnished shaft-graves entombing victims and servitors with their master, by its ideographic writing and the monopoly of bronze-founding in a small city-dwelling ruling class, Shang civilization shows many parallels to bronze-age civilization in the Near East.

In Chinese traditional history Shang kings are supposed to control the whole country, and it has been left to archaeologists to clarify the effective extent of their rule. The state appears to have been based territorially on a small area lying either side of the Yellow river in the modern Honan. The earlier capital was in the vicinity of Cheng-chou, south of the river, where excavations have been conducted since 1954, and the later at 'Great Shang' near to Anyang north of the river. The cultural succession

61,62,65, 66, 68,77

established by the typology of pottery vessels and small bronze and bone artefacts indicates four level at Cheng-chou, the last of which equates with the earlier features of the northern site. The site of Erh-li-kang belongs to the stages of Shang II and III at Cheng-chou, and Ming-kung-lu to Shang III. The city was surrounded by a massive wall constructed of thin layers (3-4 cms) of compacted earth, the method followed also in making the foundations of buildings in sector C of the city at Anyang. The latter suggests a complex of sacred and royal edifices, hallowed by numerous human sacrificial victims buried beneath them or in the adjoining precinct.

Shang civilization was centred on the plain of Honan. The political concern of its kings extended chiefly to the north and north-west, where, during the Anyang period, they appear already to have been in conflict with the Chou power that was destined to overthrow their rule. Judged by the distribution of the characteristic grey pottery, Shang influence appears to extend far to the east and southwards almost to the Yangtze, though until recently the dispersal of finds of Shang-type bronzes (chiefly vessels) indicated some extension of Shang civilization eastwards to Shantung, but not far southwards of Honan. In recent years however some impressive Shang-style bronze vessels have been discovered at places in Hunan, which shows that considerable elements of Shang culture were implanted even south of the Yangtze, in the heart of territory that was due to come under the independent rule of the princes of the Ch'u state.

79,83

The move from Cheng-chou to Anyang, dated approximately to 1400 BC, coincides with an interesting change in Shang art. Already in the Cheng-chou period the ornament of bronzes portrays almost exclusively the ferocious, evil-averting animal mask called t'ao-t'ieh, by later writers taken to mean a glutton. From the start it is an unreal animal, and the two symmetrical halves of the design which meet at the vertical ridge in the middle of the mask can be seen independently as fanciful stylizations of an animal. The latter is the k'uei dragon which in various versions provides another constant theme of Shang art. Artists of the Anyang period elaborated this stock. Their designs are rendered with seemingly endless linear complication, are exploded into their constituent parts and reunited, and are executed in two or three levels of relief. A background of somewhat squared scrolling or key-fret is now frequent (lei-wen) and animal heads, flanges and other features are made to project, though a sense of the balance and impact of the total scheme is not lost.

72,74,80 83

Shang art appears to owe nothing to the practices of the neolithic era, yet it introduces a decisive aesthetic which implies the existence of an earlier formative stage, so far unknown. It is closely bound by the limited religious and admonitory iconography which it serves, being ideally employed in the adornment of bronze vessels used in sacrifice. The potentialities of the designs and the technical methods used in achieving them (carving, and casting from carved moulds) forced it into a gradual evolution which extended beyond the Shang period almost to the end of the following Chou period. The flat linearity which dominates in Shang art is a characteristic of nearly all the art of inner Asia, including the animal art of the steppes that flourished from the sixth to the first century BC.

The object of the sacrifices conducted at the Shang capitals was primarily the gratification or appeasement of the spirits of royal ancestors. The method of taking an oracle by burning is described in the note on two ox scapulae excavated at Anyang (p. 75). together with an example of the sentences often simultaneously engraved on the bone. The names of kings gathered from such sentences make a list comparing closely with that preserved in written history. The chief deity to whom sacrifice could be offered was Ti or Shang Ti (Supreme Ti); others were Eastern Mother, Western Mother, Ruler of the Four Quarters (of Heaven). Sacrifices were made to East, West and South, but, inexplicably, not to the North. Cattle were offered to the source of the Huan river (on which the city stood). These practices combined animistic elements drawn from popular superstition with others designed to buttress the institution of kingship. Issues of peace and war, the need for rain, questions on the expected harvest, were all similarly treated.

88,8

The ritual vessels are now interpreted in the light of the oracular sentences, of inscriptions cast on the corresponding vessels of the early Chou period, and in accordance with a long tradition of ritualist lore, first codified in the third century BC, and greatly studied by antiquarians of the eleventh and twelfth centuries AD. The classification thus reached distinguishes between receptacles for sacrificial meats (flesh and grain) and wine (the black millet wine), and those intended for ritual ablution:

for preparing food ting, li, hsien	72
for holding food k'uei	114
for holding wine tsun, lei, kuang, yu, fang yi	80
for drinking chüeh, ku, chia	76
for holding ablution water p'an	73
for pouring ablution water ho, yi	91

Inscribed shoulder bones of animals and tortoise shells were excavated in large numbers at Anyang, from archives stored underground in antiquity, and the inscriptions on them are the earliest evidence for the Chinese language. Already the stock of ideographs amounted to some five thousand, more than half of which are direct ancestors of the modern script forms (i.e. as adopted in the Han revision). They are simplified representations of objects, sometimes distinguished by a similar figure standing for the class (wavy lines for water, an altar table for prayer, etc). The phallus denotes ancestor ; and the difficulty of conveying adverbs is occasionally amusingly solved, when for example 'then' or 'start to do' is transcribed as an abbreviated sign for 'person' standing by what appears to be a food-bowl on a high foot. The script principles are those common to Egyptian and Sumerian writing, such as seem to be adopted spontaneously in bronze-age societies where the need for systematic records is strongly felt.

The arms of Shang warriors are well represented in the exhibition, with the exception of the chariot, which first came into use in the latter part of the dynasty. Its construction in general resembled the Near Eastern chariots of about 1600 BC, but the many spoked wheels with slender rims are peculiar to China, as is also the system of harness employing a yoke.

In Shang ceramics, the 'corded' surface of the neolithic tradition of the east and south appear alongside smooth grey pottery with well-turned rims and foot-rings, which often copy the bronze vessels. The occasional use of pure kaolin, carved with ornament allied to that of the bronzes and above all the invention of feldspathic glaze, hold the greatest interest. The Shang kiln departs little from its neolithic predecessor, being divided clearly into stoking chamber, firing chamber, and the flue joining the two. The feldspathic glaze required a firing temperature of nearly 1200°C. With such temperatures attainable in pottery kilns, there can have been little difficulty in refining copper ore in the manufacture of bronze.

For casting the ritual vessels, elaborate piece-moulds were constructed of fired clay on which the detail had been engraved, and the molten metal was poured directly into them. There is no evidence for the method commonly practised in other bronze-age civilizations : the investment of a wax model with clay, which on firing loses the wax (the 'lost-wax' method) and retains the negative form of the desired casting, providing a one-piece mould ready to receive the molten metal. Lost-wax casting by its nature leaves no trace, but it is difficult to believe that it was not employed for certain objects, such as knives with ibex and horse-head pommels.

77

113

59

59

Bronze halberd blade *ko*, with a whirligig design on the tang, excavated in 1954 at Cheng-chou, Honan.

Length 20.3 cm
Shang dynasty : 16th–15th century BC

A bronze-bladed halberd with a haft about one metre long was the chief Shang weapon. In Shang tombs it is found in the practical form seen here, in decorated versions apparently intended as parade weapons, or in a flimsier rendering with an ornate openwork head which was evidently made specially for burial and had ritual significance, possibly in a sacrifice for rain. The *ko* is peculiarly Chinese, without parallels in adjacent bronze age cultures of like antiquity, and lacking any clear antecedent among the stone tools of the neolithic period. The blade was mounted at right angles to the haft by inserting the tang through a slot made in the wood (the substance of the haft is confirmed by traces of wood adhering to some specimens) and firmed by a peg passed through the haft and the hole of the tang. It is unlikely that this peg was of bronze since no such piece has been recovered in excavations. The upper part of the tang was often decorated, as in the present instance, with a whirligig which reappears as a frequent motif on bronze vessels of the later Shang. Illustrations of the complete weapon which are found as emblematic characters cast on bronze vessels (serving, it is thought, as a clan name or mark) show the haft with a ferrule at the lower end like a small trident, and often with a similar tripartite tassel hanging from the back of the tang. The halberd was probably carried only by foot soldiers, for it does not form part of the equipment of charioteers as observed in the burials of chariots with their drivers. Since the Shang warrior carried no sword the *ko* must have served alone for close fighting.

60

Bronze spearhead *mau,* with tubular socket, excavated in 1954 at Cheng-shou, Honan.

Length 18.5 cm
Shang dynasty : 16th–15th century BC

The Shang spearhead has distinctive features, here the oval recess in the middle of the blade, which mark it off from similar weapons made elsewhere in bronze-age Asia. Nevertheless a connexion appears to exist between the Chinese weapon and the earliest comparable spearheads made farther west. A notable parallel is with those produced in the Ural region of western Siberia, in the sphere of the Seima-Turbino culture. At intervening places in Siberia corresponding bronze spearheads have been found, as well as 'socketed axes' approximating to the Chinese design. There thus can be little doubt that contacts were established by trade between Shang China and the far west of the Asian continent, with fair indications that China was the originator of the axe, and perhaps of the spear form also.

60

61, 62

Bronze arrowheads excavated in 1953 and 1954 at Cheng-chou, Honan.

Length 6.7 cm, 6.5 cm
Shang dynasty : 16th–15th century BC

The Shang warrior was armed with a bow which had a triple curve, to judge from the shape given to it in emblematic characters cast on bronze, or from the character denoting bow written in the oracle bone script. It was therefore certainly a compound bow, constructed of several pieces, and probably of various substances, bound together. It is evident from graves of neolithic date that a compound bow was in use in Siberia at a very early time. In China direct proof of this structure is not available before the fourth century BC, but it is reasonable to assume that Chinese bows were of this kind almost from the beginning. The compound bow is short and powerful, suitable for the mounted warrior and for propelling arrows tipped with heavy bronze heads such as these. From the Shang to the Han period the evolution of the Chinese bronze arrowhead can be followed through gradual and logical stages. In the eighth century BC a three-bladed type was invented which later spread through the Central Asian steppes as the weapon of the mounted nomads. In all the stages the arrowheads have spikes for mounting in contrast to corresponding west-Asiatic socketed types, for in China bamboo provided ideal shafts.

61
62

63

Bronze knife excavated in 1954 at Cheng-chou, Honan.

Length 25.6 cm
Shang dynasty : 16th–15th century BC

Knives were seldom consigned to graves in Shang China and consequently are comparatively rare among

63

64

the surviving bronzes. When knives were buried it is noticeable that they are of an elaborate shape with clear ritual implication as instruments of animal sacrifice; or they accompany the charioteers who were buried with their vehicles and horses, in which case the pommel is shaped into a horse-head or an ibex-head. The present plain specimen owes nothing to the west-China tradition represented by the charioteers' knives, but by its tapering and upward curving blade still belongs to the large family of knives spread later through north China and beyond in Central Asia and Mongolia, to whose technical traditions China contributed so much.

64

Halberd blade *ko*, of green jade, excavated in 1955 at Cheng-chou, Honan.

Length 38 cm
Shang dynasty : 16th–15th century BC

A number of jade objects of indisputable ritual character were placed in Shang and Chou tombs. One of the chief of these was the *pi* ring (see note on number 50) and the tube of square section called *tsung*, later recognized as a symbol of the earth, is another. The significance in this respect of the jade models of halberd blades is less clear. Possibly they are to be interpreted rather as symbols of office than as instruments of sacrifice. If this is correct they then appear to be related to the oblong jade tablet called *kuei* (in some instances cut obliquely to a point at one end) which from Chou times onwards was part of the ceremonial equipment of a courtier, being held, for example, against his mouth when he spoke to the emperor.

65

Bone arrowhead excavated in 1965 at Cheng-chou, Honan.

Length 9.5 cm
Shang dynasty : 16th–15th century BC

The barbless bone arrowhead which survives from neolithic times can only have been used by the huntsman, probably for fowling.

66–69

Bone knife, comb, hairpin, and **a leftover from the carver's work** excavated in 1954–5 at Cheng-chou, Honan.

Length 11 cm, 10.1 cm, 15.3 cm, 14 cm
Shang dynasty : 16th–15th century BC

The arts of the wood-carver and bone carver flourished under the Shang dynasty. In the later period, when elephants were kept at Anyang, some ivory was available for carving vessels, as well as hairpins and ceremonial spatulas. It is noticeable that the end of the ox bone has been cut off with a bronze saw.

66

65

67

68

70

Bronze ritual wine vase *lei,* with monster mask and tortoise, excavated in 1955 at Pai-chia-chuang, Cheng-chou, Honan.

Height 25 cm

Shang dynasty: 16th–15th century BC

The shapes of some of the ritual bronze vessels of the Cheng-chou period of Shang are close to those of Lung-shan pottery in their combination of curving profile with a sharp ridge at the shoulder. The system of casting is already that of composite pottery moulds into which the molten bronze is poured directly, the detail of the ornament having been carved on the mould walls. The cruciform openings seen in the foot-rim of this piece are not explicable in detail, although in this *lei* as in some other vessel types (compare the *chüeh* number 76) it must have at least the function of supporting the core of the mould within the foot-rim. The ornament has already reached an advanced stage of formalization. The monster mask is the *t'ao-t'ieh* which characteristically lacks the lower jaw, and no doubt already at this early period had the general evil-averting and admonitory rôle ascribed to it in later literature. The scrolled ornament on either side of the mask and in the band on the shoulder is not seen as related organically to an imaginary animal of which the mask presents the head, as is the case in the later Shang period. The emblematic design of a tortoise seen on the neck resembles marks common in the later Shang which are interpretable as clan names or signs. Tortoise carapaces were also used in divination (see numbers 88 and 89).

Colour plate.

71

Bronze ritual tripod vessel *chia,* with monster mask, excavated in 1955 at Pai-chia-chuang, Cheng-chou, Honan.

Height 22 cm

Shang dynasty: 16th–15th century BC

The *chia* was appropriated to libation, joining with the *lei, chüeh, ku* and some other vessels destined for offering the black millet wine. A *t'ao-t'ieh* mask almost lost in scrolling decorates the side. Like the *chüeh* (compare number 76, and for other *chia* numbers 84 and 87) this piece has two short pillars set on the lip and carrying circular caps. The only purpose which has been proposed for these is that of lifting the vessel with tongs from the fire used to warm its contents. The complication of mould parts required to cast the *chia* is even more striking than in the simpler vases. The tense profile is carefully contrived and in keeping with the triangular section and points of the legs.

72

Bronze ritual tripod vessel *ting,* with monster mask, excavated in 1955 at Pai-chia-chuang, Cheng-chou, Honan.

Height 19 cm

Shang dynasty: 16th–15th century BC

This *ting* stands at the head of a long line of descent in which the vessel form retained its pre-eminence among

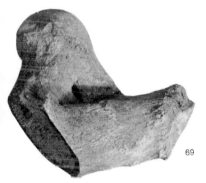

69

70 (DW)

70A

71 (DW)

the ritual bronzes while varying its ornament and proportions in response to the slow evolution of the hieratic style. The tall sides and perfectly spherical base, as well as the pointed legs, mark it as archaic. The *t'ao-t'ieh* mask appears with lateral extensions which resemble a body of the monster, doubled on either side for symmetry and allusively treated for purely decorative effect. It is significant for the later development of this motif that the body is approximately divided into three horizontal parts, and that each body with its half of the mask begins to assume the appearance of a separate animal, the dragon called *k'uei*. The flat and comparatively wide surface of the raised bands of the design is characteristic of the art of the Cheng-chou period (see number 75).

73

Bronze ritual basin *p'an*, with monster mask, excavated in 1955 at Pai-chia-chuang, Cheng-chou, Honan.

Height 10.5 cm, diameter 30 cm
Shang dynasty : 16th–15th century BC

The later ritualists describe the *p'an* as used for ceremonial washing. Its connexion with a pottery form of the Lung-shan period is close, although it stands on a foot-rim and not a high foot (compare number 55). In the decoration on the side the monster mask, *t'ao-t'ieh*, has become so far dissolved in the scrolled additions which accompany it that little more than its eye appears.

74

Bronze ritual wine vase *tsun*, with monster mask, excavated in 1954 at Cheng-chou, Honan.

Height 24.9 cm
Shang dynasty : 16th–15th century BC

As a name for a class of ritual vessels the term *tsun*, adopted by antiquarians of the Sung dynasty, includes wide vases of this type and some vases in the shape of animals. The decoration of this piece differs from that of the *lei* (number 70) in adding lateral flanges somewhat re-

sembling the *k'uei* dragons which sometimes flank the protective *t'ao-t'ieh* mask, and in placing in high relief on the shoulder further masks which share bovine and feline features. That they are more likely to have originated as bull masks rendered fierce by assimilation to the tiger than as imitations of the tiger itself, is suggested by the inclination of hieratic art to decorate sacrificial vessels with the representation of the animal sacrificed. Sacrificial tigers seem improbable, and vessels are known in which the bovine mask is clearly identified. But another theory would see an actual tiger as the origin of the *t'ao-t'ieh*, adopted as guardian against evil spirits and as destroyer of animals which consumed the crops.

75

Bronze ritual vessel *li*, with lobed body and ornament of *k'uei* dragons, excavated in 1955 at Pai-chia-chuang, Cheng-chou, Honan.

Height 16.5 cm
Shang dynasty : 16th–15th century BC

75 (DW)

As a ceramic form the *li* is characteristic of Lung-shan culture, and in bronze it is more frequent in the earlier Shang period than later. Its ritual function was similar to that of the normal *ting* tripod, the preparation of the sacrificial meats. In this piece the flat-topped relief of the ornament and the manner of its abstraction from real animal form is typical of the Cheng-chou work of early Shang (compare number 72). The motif termed *k'uei* dragon was so named by antiquarians of the Sung dynasty who believed it to represent a mythological creature mentioned in pre-Han texts, which was connected with rain-making and was said to have only one leg. For its graphic derivation from the *t'ao-t'ieh* mask see number 72.

76

Bronze ritual goblet *chüeh*, with decoration of a monster mask, excavated in 1965 at Ming-kung-lu, Cheng-chou, Honan.

Height 17.2 cm
Shang dynasty : 16th–15th century BC

76

The *chüeh*, a frequent accompaniment of the *ku* goblet (compare number 112), is the strangest of the Shang bronzes, whose mention in oracle texts appears to guarantee the identification of the name with the vessel type. The character is composed of a bird-like element combined with a hand, being no doubt a combination of indicator and phonetic; but the lexicographer of the *Shuo wen* (second century AD) assumed that the ancient goblet was shaped like a bird and moralised the name by transcribing it with homophones meaning 'sufficiency' and 'restraint'. In the *Yi li* the *chüeh* is named as the appropriate libation cup for thirteen ceremonies. It has been suggested that it owes its shape to a rustic prototype consisting of a horn or gourd supported in an upright position by two attached legs. The capped columns on the lip (mostly a pair, rarely a single column) may have given purchase to tongs used in lifting the goblet from the fire when the black wine was heated in it (see number 71). The flat bottom, thin

77 (DW)

78

sides and slender legs, as well as the style of ornament, place this piece in the early Shang period.

77

Pottery steamer *hsien*, with corded surface, excavated in 1953 at Cheng-chou, Honan.

Height 40 cm
Shang dynasty: 16th–15th century BC

This looks like a combination of two vessels, a *li* beneath and a typical Shang coarse bowl with hand-shaped body and wheel-turned rim above. The bronze versions of this vessel have a pierced partition separating the upper and lower chambers, and were evidently intended like the *ting* and *li* for cooking sacrificial meats. No *hsien* are known from the neolithic period, although neolithic bowls with perforated bottoms appear to be intended for setting on top of the normal *li*. The ancient character for the *hsien* consists of *li* combined with a phonetic element which in some cases is the ideogram for dog. Consequently the fanciful Han lexicographer writes: 'a temple dog was called *keng hsien*. Fat ones were offered in sacrifice'! (See numbers 88 and 89.)

78

Pottery vase with rounded bottom, *tsun*, excavated in 1964 at Cheng-chou, Honan.

Height 34.5 cm
Shang dynasty: 16th–15th century BC

Although the Shang potter possessed a fast wheel she often used it only for shaping the rim and the foot-rim of her pots. The body of the vessel in this instance has been made by the immemorial method of beating the clay with a criss-crossed paddle against a stone, and the rim trued and given a characteristic Shang profile on the wheel. The predominance of grey-bodied ware in central China, in neolithic, Shang and later times, is a phenomenon independent of the distribution of the finer red and black wares on which the classification of neolithic cultures rests, and betokens the continued stability of population on the middle course of the Yellow river.

79

Bronze four-legged ritual food vessel *ting*, decorated with human faces, excavated in 1965 at Ning-hsiang, Hunan.

Height 38.7 cm
Shang dynasty: 14th–11th century BC

Sometimes the victim of the sacrifice was portrayed on the side of the ritual vessel. This is the case with two *ting* decorated with realistic deer and bull heads. On this piece the allusion is to human sacrifice, which is attested besides in oracle sentences concerning offerings to be made to ancestors. Human beings were killed also to make great funerals, or buried in pits below the foundations of important buildings. Prisoners of war were reduced to slavery and no doubt supplied the victims of holocausts. On the other hand the inscription *ta ho*, signifying 'large grain', may indicate what the *ting* was des-

70 (DW)

79A

tined to hold in the rite. The Shang representations of the human face are fairly uniform in a convention probably meant to represent an enemy. The massive hooked flanges seen at the corners of this *ting* are a characteristic of the latest phase of Shang, and of the early Western Chou period. They occur at joints of the mould parts, and make a virtue of projections that must sometimes have been produced unintentionally in casting.

80

Bronze ritual wine vessel *tsun*, excavated in 1957 at Fu-nan, Anhui.

Height 47 cm
Shang dynasty: 14th–11th century BC

In the perfection of its ornament and the 'water patina' bespeaking ideal preservation below ground, this *tsun* is one of the most remarkable pieces to have been recovered. It brings proof that the bronze casters of Anhui were not inferior to those of the Shang capital at Anyang. They followed the same method of securing the mould core within the foot-ring that was used in the Anyang ateliers, as shown by the cruciform perforations (compare for example number 112). But the artistic style is distinct: here the slightly rounded relief imparts a rich movement to the design in comparison with which the layered relief of Anyang is static and austere. The tiger masks on the shoulder repeat a familiar motif, but the

80 (DW)

openwork figures projecting as flanges and separating the heads are strange, though they seem to allude remotely to the *k'uei* dragon.

Colour plate.

81

Bronze ritual wine bucket in the shape of addorsed owls, *hsiao yu*, excavated in 1957 at Shih-lou, Shansi.

Height including handle 19.7 cm
Shang dynasty : 14th–11th century BC

Receptacles for the libation wine made in the shape of animals were not uncommon in the later Shang. Many of these represent the owl, which in earlier Chinese tradition appears to have had favourable associations. It may have symbolized a helper among spirits of the underworld, for it might be thought to guide well in the dark. Unlike the other birds of the Shang decorative stock the owl is always represented more or less naturally. The owl *tsun* is shaped either as a single bird or, as here, two birds back to back. Later the owl acquired a worse reputation, and, for eating its mother, was taken as an exemplar of filial impiety.

81

82

Bronze ritual wine mixer in the shape of a monster, *kuang*, decorated with a dragon, excavated in 1959 at Shih-lou, Shansi.

Length 41.5 cm
Shang dynasty : 14th–11th century BC

The *kuang*, whose more usual shape is seen in number 90, was in later tradition reputed to be a receptacle for mixing the sacrificial wine, and the ladle and internal partition seen in some specimens bears out this view. This piece is unique, having only the monster head in common with the standard type. The 'bottle horns' of the head perhaps copy the blunted and capped horns of cattle led as victims to sacrifice. Snake-like dragons are a frequent adornment of the side of *kuang*. A crocodile, as seen from above, is depicted on the side of the vessel with exceptional naturalism, and lends support to the view that this animal is the reality behind the conventional design of the *k'uei* dragon.*

81 (CG)

83

Bronze square-bodied ritual wine vase *tsun*, excavated in 1963 at Ch'ang-ning, Hunan.

Height 53.8 cm
Shang dynasty : 14th–11th century BC

The decoration of the *tsun* marks a final stage in the evolution of bronze ornament in the Shang period. The *t'ao-t'ieh* monster masks, having first been immersed in a compact mass of spiral lines, were later raised in relief against this ground. The various components, eyes, eyebrows, ears, horns etc., remained separated and might be widely scattered in the design. The notched flanges which follow the joints of the mould parts are given an important rôle in defining the shape. On the

82 (DW)

82A

shoulder stand birds whose bodies resemble those of owl-shaped vessels, but the heads are nearer to the ox or buffalo heads with blunted and capped horns which figure frequently on the ritual bronzes.

83

84

Bronze ritual wine vessel *chia*, excavated in 1965 at Fei-hsi, Anhui.

Height 55.3 cm
Shang dynasty : 14th–11th century BC

The *chia* is decorated with two bands in which *t'ao-t'ieh* monster masks, largely resolved into linear figures, alternate in upright and inverted position. (Compare numbers 71 and 87.)

85

Bronze ritual wine bucket *yu*, inscribed *pei kan* (?), excavated in 1950 at Anyang, Honan.

Height including handle 29 cm
Shang dynasty : 14th–11th century BC

The later phase of Shang bronze manufacture has greater variety and elegance of shapes, with linear elaboration of ornament and relief effects, and more frequently inscriptions are cast on the vessels. The latter are rarely intelligible in terms of the later writing, often being more complicated and pictorial, and in many cases can be interpreted as clan names. The emblematic characters are nevertheless more formalized than they appear to have been in the Cheng-chou period (compare number 70). On the *yu* the inscription is equivalent to later ideograms giving the meaning 'northern shield', and must be a personal designation. The *yu* with its high handle is an invention of late Shang, probably belonging to the later occupation at Anyang, its successive shapes passing smoothly into designs belonging to the Western Chou.

86

Bronze four-legged ritual food vessel *ting*, inscribed *Father chi*, excavated in 1950 at Anyang, Honan.

Height 21.7 cm
Shang dynasty : 14th–11th century BC

Among the sacrificial food-vessels of the later Shang the *ting* holds pride of place. In the latest phase they are rectangular, and of sizes reaching exceptionally to a height of 1.73 metres and a weight of 700 kilogrammes (the Ssŭ-mu-wu *ting*). Rectangular *ting* continued to be made until about the middle of the tenth century BC, their decoration nicely illustrating the change from late Shang to Western Chou style. In this piece versions of the *t'ao-t'ieh* monster mask are placed at the top of the legs, but in the key-fret and nipples of the sides only decorative effect appears to be sought. The birds are of a typical Shang design, distinct from those derived from the Chou repertory of mythological motifs, thought to originate in western China, which are successively transformed in the succeeding two centuries (compare numbers 92 and 93). It is possible that the bird symbolizes the wind deity

84

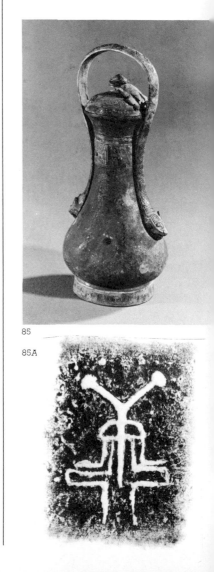

85

85A

86 (DW)

mentioned in oracle sentences, or is an ancestor of the auspicious phoenix (*feng-huang*) of the later lore. The inscription appropriates this vessel to sacrifice made to an ancestor designated *Father chi*. In ritual usage ancestors were named according to the day on which an offering was made to them, *chi* in this case denoting the sixth day of the ten-day cycle.

Colour plate.

87

Bronze ritual wine vessel chia, inscribed *Mother ya*, excavated in 1959 at Anyang, Honan.

Height 30.8 cm
Shang dynasty : 14th–11th century BC

The main zone of decoration typifies the flat graphic style which seems to stand at the beginning of the transformation of the hieratic motifs in the later Shang period. The *t'ao-t'ieh*, clearly separable into two confronted *k'uei* dragons, is about to be dissolved into the ground of compact squared spirals called 'thunder pattern' from their resemblance to an ideograph. In the band at the neck this idea is repeated, with *k'uei* of a distinct double-bodied kind. The triangular motif set over this band is stylized from the figure of a cicada, a common Shang device, which may symbolize rebirth in an underworld, or the earth and the underworld itself. In the ritual texts of a later period the term *chia* refers to wine receptacle, but it has been attached to the form described here only since the Sung period. *Ya* appears to be a ceremonial name applied to the female ancestor to whom offering was to be made with the *chia*.

88, 89

Two ox scapulae treated for oracle-taking, excavated in 1971 at Anyang, Honan.

Length 37 cm, 40.5 cm
Shang dynasty : 14th–11th century BC

Each scapula shows small pits gouged with a chisel to the edge of which a heated bronze point has been applied. From the shape of the forked cracks so caused on the other side of the bone answers were read to the questions which are inscribed. Among the cracks a characteristic line with a short spur gave the shape for the ideograph *pu* ⼘ , 'to take an oracle'. The inscribed sentences concern the proper choice of animal victims for sacrifice to ancestors denoted by the number of a day (their offering day) in the ten-day cycle. The language is abbreviated and technical. The sentence on the left-hand scapula reads something like :

> Get ready the officers. Father Second a pig, son a pig ; Mother Ninth a pig. Get ready the overseers. Third, in a *ting* vessel, a dog. Fourth a pig. Ancestor Seventh a pig. Father Second a pig, son a pig.

Each proposal for a sacrifice was checked by reference to the result of one operation of burning and cracking the bone, and proceeded with if the oracle consented. The prominence of pork in the economy is obvious. These scapulae were found together with nineteen others, being stored as archives or for further use.

86 A

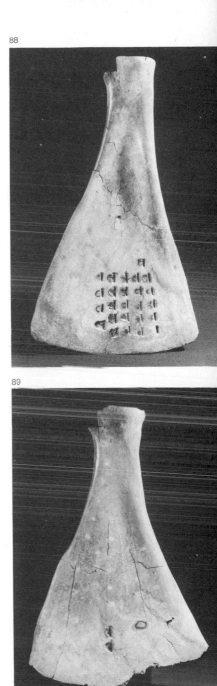

88

89

87

87A

3

西周、春秋

Western Chou dynasty
1027-771 BC

Period of the Spring and Autumn Annals
770-475 BC

After the Chou defeat of the Shang state in 1027 BC (traditional date 1122 BC) the territory of central China was divided among some scores of princelings who owed allegiance to the central Chou state but increasingly asserted their independence. Bronze casting was wider spread, the courts of the 'feudal' rulers producing ritual vessels no less than the Chou capital. The range of vessel shapes is now smaller (notably the *chüeh*, *chia* and *ku* disappear) but at first the *t'ao-t'ieh* masks and dragons of Shang ornament continue in use. Gradually, in a process complete by the late ninth century BC, the explicit animal motifs are replaced by geometricised figures which are derived from them by simplification and further formalization. For example, some of the dragon-derived figures seen on the *loi* number 95 suggest the origin of the totally unrepresentational figures covering the *hu* number 94. Simultaneously the relief takes on a new appearance, with much use of grooved bands. Some of the abstractions arise from the device of paired birds with intertwining crests and tails, a favourite decoration in the early Chou decades, belonging to a distinct Chou repertory. Literacy expands under the Chou, long and historically circumstantial inscriptions appearing on the bronze vessels. Despite the charge of barbarism brought against them in conventional Chinese history the forbears of the Chou rulers of central China cannot have stood lower culturally than the Shang themselves. The rulers of the principalities occupied walled cities (T'an, near Ch'eng-tzü-yai in Shantung has been excavated) and defended them by the bow, halberd and chariot in a technique of warfare scarcely differing from that of the preceding dynasty.

The artistic interest of the Western Chou period is concentrated in the late eleventh and the tenth

97

(DW)

century BC. A new sombre emphasis invests the traditional designs of *kuang, tsun, ting* and *fang-yi*, particularly as they appear in the bronze treasure of Fu-feng, a site in Shensi where the individuality of a west-China tradition is felt. Other styles with local currency make their appearance for the first time, such as that represented by vessels from T'un-hsi in Anhui. In the design of harness trappings and bronze knives some entirely new motifs are adopted in the northern territories under Western Chou influence, such as stylized heads of birds of prey, and the theme of an animal-in-a-ring, which came to be adopted by China's neighbours in the Central Asian steppes and in south Siberia. Towards 500 BC a revised version of animal ornament in bands is the dominant characteristic of a new casting tradition launched in Shansi, and best known from discoveries made at Li-yü and the later site of Hou-ma. Towards the end of the Period of the Spring and Autumn Annals sets of bronze bells tend to oust other bronzes from tombs, although they are still accompanied by *ting* tripods, basins, and wine containers (*hu, tsun* etc) of various shapes.

Technology   ITEMS 112–123

Technical advances in various fields occurred in the late sixth and early fifth century, at the end of the Period of the Spring and Autumn Annals and the beginning of the Period of the Warring States. It is appropriate to review the history of casting and high-fired ceramics at this point in the exhibition sequence, so that items illustrating these sides of technology from the fifteenth to the fourth century BC are grouped together here.

The evidence for the use of multi-part piece-moulds in direct casting for the production of the early bronze vessels is seen – apart from surviving fragments of the moulds themselves – in joint-lines traceable in the cast ornament, the presence of chaplets employed to separate the outer mould from the core, and possibly in such a device as the cruciform perforation found in the side of *ku* and in the foot-ring of some *kuei*. Direct casting persisted as the only or the main technique until the fifth century BC, but then it was rapidly replaced by lost-wax casting (see p. 63 above) which equally subserved and promoted the development of the decorative style of the Period of the Warring States, the so-called Huai style. The great mask-and-ring demonstrates this method in an elaborate work. In north China, at Hou-ma in Shansi, there was however conservative adherence to direct casting until a later date, probably the earlier fourth century BC. Proof of this lies in the many clay mould parts and patterns which were found there in excavations. The patterns represent a first stage in one method of mould-making, the moulds being negative impressions taken from the positive original. In the Shang period this was sometimes the procedure, although the more usual method was to carve ornament on mould parts as the first step.

A phase of hard-glaze ceramics posterior to the Shang product is indicated by the finds at T'un-hsi in Anhui. Subsequently the glazing technique may have been temporarily lost. Finds of similarly glazed vessels do not recur until the late fourth or third century BC, by which time a tradition of feldspathic glazing is established in the region of the Yangtze mouth, where it was due to flourish for a thousand years. On the eve of the Han dynasty low-fired lead-fluxed glaze makes a first appearance, the ultimate sequel to which is the lead-glazed pottery of the Sui and T'ang periods, noted in Section Ten.

The first use of iron in China should probably be dated about 500 BC. Although a famous literary reference places sophisticated iron-casting about twenty years earlier, archaeological evidence to date does not bear this out, but points to a beginning in the fifth century. The much repeated statement that in China iron-casting preceded forging is also open to question. But it is certain that casting was not much later, if at all, than forging, probably being practised also from the fifth century BC. Casting was thus earlier in China than in Europe by about seventeen centuries. From the third century BC long forged iron swords displaced the bronze swords which had been the classic weapon of the two previous centuries, and being placed in the hands of huge infantry armies added their toll to the exacerbated warfare of the later part of the Period of the Warring States.

90 (DW)

93 (DW)

93A

91 (DW)

92

90

Bronze ritual wine mixer *kuang,* in the shape of a monster, inscribed *jih chi,* excavated in 1963 at Fu-feng Shensi.

Height 31.6 cm
Western Chou dynasty : 10th century BC

The *kuang* regularly bears a head compounded of tiger and ox or water buffalo, the 'bottle horns' being the blunted horns of the sacrificial victim. The head and back make a lid, which being removed leaves a spouted jug from which wine could be poured. The designation *kuang* was first applied to this shape of vessel at the beginning of the present century, the Sung dynasty cataloguers having been content to class it with the vessel shaped like a sauce-boat which is called *yi* and served to hold water for ceremonial hand washing. The *kuang* belongs to the beginning of the Western Chou period and displays the weighty grotesque of the early Chou style. Serpents and *t'ao-t'ieh* are included in its decoration. The inscription means 'sixth day' and refers to the offering day of the ancestor to whom the vessel was assigned (see number 86). A date for this *kuang* in the early tenth century BC is probable.

91

Bronze ritual wine pourer *ho,* excavated in 1963 at Fu-feng, Shensi.

Height 38 cm
Western Chou dynasty : 9th century BC

Some of the most eccentric and incongruous inventions of the Chou bronze masters are seen in the spouted vessels which are made throughout the dynasty. Here the bird, tiger and monster adapted as spout are alien to the Shang idiom. The motifs which fill the circles on the sides are derived from the *k'uei* dragon, and the whirligig at the centre is familiar in the earlier period.

92

Bronze square-bodied ritual wine vessel *tsun,* inscribed *jih chi,* excavated in 1963 at Fu-feng, Shensi.

Height 29.5 cm
Western Chou dynasty : 10th century BC

The *t'ao-t'ieh* monster mask, reconstituted after its stylistic dismemberments in the late Shang style (compare number 83), is interpreted in the high rounded relief and with the added grotesque projections which are typical of early Chou style, and in this piece indicate a date in the early tenth century BC. The prevalence of stylized birds in the decoration is another Chou feature which derives from the west-China tradition. For the inscription see number 90.

93

Bronze rectangular ritual vessel with lid *fang yi,* inscribed for *jih chi,* excavated in 1963 at Fu-feng, Shensi.

Height 38.5 cm
Western Chou dynasty : 10th century BC

The purpose of the *fang-yi* (a latter-day name meaning only 'square ritual vessel') is unknown, but it is often described as a receptacle for wine. Earlier examples of this form, always with large monster masks on the sides, appear to go back to the early phase of the Anyang period of Shang, but not to the Cheng-chou period. In this instance the modelling of the *t'ao-t'ieh* masks and the fantasy of wide hooked flanges indicate early Chou date, probably in the early tenth century BC. In translation the inscription reads: 'For the august deceased Father Sixth Day, a precious ritual vessel to be placed in the ancestral temple, to be treasured in prominent use for a myriad years and in perpetuity by sons and grandsons'. For the ritual designation 'sixth day' see number 90.

Colour plate.

94

Bronze ritual wine vessel *hu*, inscribed for *chi-fu*, excavated in 1960 at Fu-feng, Shensi.

Height 59.4 cm
Western Chou dynasty : late 9th century BC

In shape and ornaments the *hu* marks a sharp departure from the ritual tradition. The large wave design cannot be derived from the permutation of stylized dragons, although something of these persists in the bands of ornament at the top and the foot-rim. The inscription cast on the vessel reads (with two uncertain phrases omitted):
On the auspicious day *keng wu* in the fifth month, T'ung Chung residing in the Western Palace made gift to Chi Fu of six . . ., four households of serfs, ten *chun* weight of gold. Chi Fu bowed his head to the ground, uttered a prayer for the prosperity of our sovereign, then to commemorate this occasion made this . . . ritual *hu*. Chi Fu was pious. May his descendants treasure this vessel in use for a myriad years.
The identity of the first gift is differently interpreted, as 'shield bearers', and as 'green reeds' intended for sipping the ceremonial wine.

95

Bronze ritual wine vessel *lei*, with decoration of *k'uei* dragons, excavated at Fu-feng, Shensi.

Height 46.1 cm
Western Chou dynasty : about 900 BC

The ornament consists of a revived version of the *k'uei* dragon arranged in blade-shaped panels such as the earlier Shang artist filled with a conventional design of the cicada.

96

Bronze ritual food vessel *kuei*, inscribed for *yü fu kuei* excavated in 1955 at K'o-tso, Liao-ning.

Height 16.1 cm
Western Chou dynasty : late 11th century or 10th century BC

The context of this *kuei* as excavated places it in the Western Chou period, but its shape and decorative style

95 (DW)

94 (DW)
94 A

96

96A

belong to the late Shang idiom. In Liao-ning this style appears to have survived into the post-Shang period unaffected by the innovations which are to be observed in central China. The inscription begins with an emblematic fish (*yü*) and names 'Father Tenth Day' as the ancestor for whose offerings the *kuei* is to be used. See number 86 for the significance of this ritual name. Number 115 comes from the same site.

97

Bronze ritual wine bucket *yu*, inscribed by *Kung*, excavated in 1965 at T'un-hsi, Anhui.

Height including handle 23.5 cm
Western Chou dynasty: 11th century–early 10th century BC

Intertwining of parts of the design was scrupulously avoided in the Shang schemes of decoration, but introduced into central China in the first decades of the Western Chou period, together with the elaborate birds which the Chou style favoured. The *k'uei* dragons with reverted head which fill the band at the neck of the vessel equally betoken the Chou tradition and with the birds indicate an early post-Shang date. The agitated movement of the design contrasts with the static quality of the earlier hieratic decoration. The inscription reads in translation: 'Kung has made this precious ritual vessel to be used in perpetuity by sons and grandsons'.

98

Bronze ritual food vessel *kuei*, excavated in 1966 at T'un-hsi, Anhui.

Height 19.7 cm, diameter 27.2 cm
Western Chou dynasty: 10th century BC

The decoration of this piece departs wholly from the normal style of Western Chou, which deals generally with permutations of bird motifs and with non-representational figures abstracted from them and from the *k'uei* dragon. The geometric system of this ornament is without parallel. But in the central design, and in the filling of the band at neck and foot-ring, are seen remnants of *t'ao-t'ieh* monster mask and *k'uei* dragons, while the handles attenuate the normal Western Chou device: a deer-like animal head with suggestions of bird in the crest and lower appendage. The latter normally show explicit claws, which are here turned into a meaningless figure. These features indicate the provincial relation of the Anhui atelier to the main tradition as preserved in bronzes made for the Chou court, and suggest a date in the late tenth or the ninth century BC.

Colour plate.

98 (DW)

99

99

Bronze ritual basin *p'an*, excavated in 1959 at T'un-hsi, Anhui.

Height 9.4 cm, diameter 31.6 cm
Western Chou dynasty: 10th century BC

The compression of *k'uei* dragons into continuous design in the bands of ornament shows the motif well on its way

97A

97 (DW

to becoming the diaper of minute figures which is a constant resource of the artist in the later Chou period. This piece was probably made about 1000 BC.

100

Bronze ritual vase *hu,* decorated with serpents and tigers, excavated in 1961 at Hou-ma, Shansi.

Height 86.6 cm
Spring and Autumn : 6th or early 5th century BC

The decoration of this *hu* marks the beginning of a new phase of art which a piece like the *hsi ting* number 111 anticipates by the liberties it takes with traditional practice. At the neck is a zone of figures derived from a continuous band of interlacing dragons which was due in the sequel to be reduced in scale to the rôle of a diaper suited to filling major surfaces. Intertwined snakes take up a graphic method already present in the Western Chou period (compare number 95) which was due to be much exploited in the so-called Huai style of the fifth–third centuries. Most curious is the treatment of the tigers sipping at the lip, shaping the handles and clinging to the sides to emphasize the angularity of the form. They are composed of a mass of short spiral figures incorporating dimples (which suggest recesses for inlay though none has been found). At about this time a tiger with spiral nose, crescentic feet and marked with spirals on shoulder and haunch was becoming popular in the art of the nomads on the north-west borders of China and on the Central Asian steppes. It is debated whether this connexion of Chinese art with territories beyond her borders was a case of influence accepted or exerted ; in either case the exchange was fruitful for both traditions.

101

Bronze basin *chien*, decorated with monster masks and the dragon diaper *p'an chih*, excavated in 1961 at Hou-ma, Shansi.

Height 36.8 cm, diameter 76 cm
Spring and Autumn : late 6th or early 5th century BC

The process of reducing the scale of the continuous dragon pattern, mentioned in the note on number 99, has been taken a stage farther. The masks, while fulfilling an ancient rôle, are a new invention. The basin no doubt served for ritual ablution, and so was dignified for inclusion in rich grave gifts. The *chien* was a bowl for general purposes. The *Chou li* says of it : 'In early spring the *chien* are set out . . . warm foods are inspected in them, and . . . wine likewise. In the sacrificial rites an ice *chien* is also supplied', which suggests that no very clear idea was entertained about it. Because the ideograph for the basin was the same as that used for mirror, antiquarians also supposed that the *chien* filled with water was used for reflection.

100 (DW)

101

102-110

102–110

Nine bronze bells tuned in scale, *pien chung,* from the tomb of a Marquis of Ts'ai at Shou-hsien, Anhui, excavated in 1965.

Height from 28 to 16.6 cm
Spring and Autumn : First quarter of the 5th century BC

Shou-hsien on the Huai river near its confluence with the Yangtze was an important city in the state of Wu, and still continued to flourish after the invasion by Yüeh in 493 BC and the subsequent annexation by Ch'u. By 493 BC the neighbouring small state of Ts'ai had been occupied by Ch'u, and a Marquis Chao of Ts'ai had taken refuge in Wu. Many of the bronze vessels excavated from the Shou-hsien tomb are inscribed with the title of a Marquis of Ts'ai who is either the first refugee from his territory, or a near successor, and therefore the tomb may be dated to the first quarter of the fifth century. Bells of the kind represented here had been made in China since the tenth century BC. when they appear in the ancient Chou homeland in the north-west. The bells are intended to be hung and struck on the nipples which line the sides, there being no internal clapper. Between the nipples a panel is usually reserved for inscription, as here, and the field below given over to a scheme of decoration based on the *t'ao-t'ieh* monster mask or its graphic derivatives. The sacred character of the *chung* thus proclaimed, they were used in ceremonial music, particularly, it appears, in music performed at the princes' courts. The bells from the Ts'ai tomb were made in the life span traditionally allotted to Confucius, and we may think of such instruments as these sounding in the music of the Succession Dance, which, when first he heard it in the state of Ch'i, moved the sage so greatly that for three months 'he did not know the taste of meat', i.e. notice what he was eating (see number 257). Confucius' attention to music appears in another passage: 'When the Master was in company with a person who was singing, if he sang well, he would make him repeat the song, while he accompanied with his own voice' (Legge's translation).

The bells were tuned to a scale, the notes determined approximately by the size being made more exact by chiselling away some metal inside. Although bells have often been found in groups the accurate composition of a musical set is not certain, for the corrosion of the bronze destroys the note and evidently no obligation was felt to include a complete series whenever bells were buried with their owners. The most promising set is that found in a tomb at Hsin-yang in Honan, consisting of thirteen well-preserved bells giving very closely the notes:

The highest bell may be a rogue, for it not only jumps a greater interval than any other, but also introduces the possibility of a tritone, which is avoided elsewhere. At least in the more audible part of the scale the Chinese apparently agreed with occidental musicians that *Mi contra fa est diabolus in musica*. The Ts'ai series as it survives may have produced this scale, or perhaps only part of it, for two steps in size rather greater than the rest may mean that bells are missing from the set. On the other hand another set consisting of nine bells has recently been excavated (see number 124).

111

Bronze ritual vessel in the shape of an animal, *hsi ting*, with a lid, excavated in 1959 at Shu-ch'eng, Anhui.

Height 27.5 cm
Spring and Autumn : 7th or early 6th century BC

The designer of ritual bronzes conservatively retained ancient decorative and symbolic motifs in the ornament of vessels even when shapes departed arbitrarily from ancient standards. This tripod is an invention of a time

111 (DW)

when bronze art was on the threshold of revolutionary change. No such deer-like victim represented as a tripod receptacle is known from the Shang or Western Chou period; but the serpent coiled on the side is a good Shang motif, and the figures in the band of ornament reproduce the early Chou graphic derivatives of *k'uei* dragons. The hooked flange at the back repeats the idea of the ancient feature but shows a misunderstanding of the exact permissible forms.

112

112

Bronze ritual breaker *ku*, decorated with a monster mask, excavated in 1965 at Ming-kung-lu, Cheng-chou, Honan.

Height 18 cm
Shang dynasty: 16th–15th century BC

The combination of a *ku* with a *chüeh* (compare number 76) as libation cups is the most frequent grave-gift of ritual vessels found in Shang tombs, occurring even in the humbler sort and often in pottery versions. From the Cheng-chou period onwards the *ku* gains in elegance of slender, curving profile and exact rendering of minute relief ornament, the type represented by this piece standing at the beginning of the series. Nearly all the specimens have at the middle a zone with horizontal raised lines and two cruciform perforations opposite each other, situated just below a bronze partition which forms the bottom of the containing part of the beaker. As in the case of the *lei* number 70 these perforations are thought to have served in some unexplained manner to adjust the mould core which ensured the hollow base of the casting. But perhaps a symbolic meaning is intended, for a similar perforation is known on an ivory cup. Here the *t'ao-t'ieh* with its lateral extensions is in the established early style. In *Analects* VI.23 Confucius exclaims 'a *ku* that is no *ku* . . .', apparently deploring the corruption of ancient tradition which had produced the political chaos of his day. The *ku* was not made after the fall of the house of Shang, and of surviving *chüeh* only a few can be dated in the opening decades of the Western Chou period.

113

113

Glazed pottery vase with carinated shoulder and flaring mouth, excavated in 1965 at Ming-kung-lu, Cheng-chou, Honan.

Height 28.2 cm
Shang dynasty: 16th–15th century BC

Pottery of this class is the earliest known ware covered with a high-fired, feldspathic glaze. The body is of near stoneware hardness, and above the ridged shoulder is impressed with a lozenge pattern characteristic of Shang. Below it are the marks of cords traditional on the neolithic and later pottery of central and south-east China. The even spread of the glaze and its presence below the projection of the shoulder is proof that it is not fortuitous. The view that the glaze resulted from a kiln accident was held formerly by those unable to accept this early invention in China of a revolutionary technique which was developed gradually towards the porcelains of Sung, but in Europe could not be imitated before the eighteenth century.

114

114A

114

Bronze ritual food vessel *kuei*, inscribed *pei kan ko*, excavated in 1950 from the royal tomb at Wu-kuan-ts'un, Anyang, Honan.

Height 14.7 cm
Shang dynasty: 14th–11th century BC

The simple bowl on a foot-ring, imitated from the pottery bowl, was made chiefly in the later Shang period. The type without handles is particularly frequent in Honan (an example is number 96), while the *kuei* with double ring handles appears to be a west-China form which reached Anyang just before the Chou invasion of central China. The *kuei* is chief among the ritual containers intended for preparing and holding sacrificial meats. This specimen is decorated with tiger masks in high relief separated by a frieze of silkworms, a reminder of the importance which silk had already acquired in Shang economy.

115

Bronze ritual wine bucket *yu*, inscribed by *Shih-shu*, excavated in 1955 at K'o-tso, Liao-ning.

Height 28.5 cm
Western Chou dynasty: Late 11th century or 10th century BC

The *yu* of relaxed profile belongs to the opening decades of the Western Chou period. The deer-like heads at the swivels of the handle are peculiar to the period. In the bands of ornament the *k'uei* dragon is chiefly noticeable by its eye. The lid is intended to serve as a goblet and so has a handle which can serve as a foot-ring. The inscription reads: 'Shih-shu has made this ritual vessel for Father Ninth Day', For the ritual designation of the ancestor see number 86. Number 96 comes from the same site.

116 118

Brown glazed pottery excavated in 1965 at T'un-hsi, Anhui.

Height 11 cm, 11.9 cm, 16 cm
Western Chou dynasty: 9th–8th century BC

The bowls with triple lugs and horizontal grooves, and with double lugs and criss-crossed shoulder, are not unlike pieces made at this time in plain pottery. The bottle-shaped vase is a less usual shape. After the episodes of feldspathic glazing at Cheng-chou and Anyang in the Shang period (see number 113), glazed pottery is only fitfully represented in the archaeological record before the middle of the Han dynasty. The large production at T'un-hsi is exceptional and it is likely that the ware was traded farther afield. The ornament is of stamped and incised geometric figures, roughly executed. Some of the pieces carry a potter's mark such as a double arrow. The glaze, though feldspathic, adheres less well to the body than in the case of the Shang glazed ware, a technical difference which suggests that the tradition was not unbroken. The glaze varies in colour and viscosity from a thick dark brown to a thinner olive green. Considering the relatively high

115

115A

116

117

118

119
119A

cost of firing this pottery to its maturing temperature of about 1200° Centigrade, it is remarkable that more care was not spent on its fashioning. The kilns were active at T'un-hsi about 800 BC.

119

Iron twin mould for casting sickle-blades, in 1953 at Hsing-lung, Hopei.

Length 32.5 cm
Warring States : 5th–4th century BC

The facility acquired in China before 500 BC in pouring and casting iron as opposed to forging it made possible the manufacture of complicated and exact shapes in the metal, in a manner not emulated in Europe until the twelfth century AD. A peculiar technique was that of employing iron moulds for casting other metal objects, in this case sickle-blades. These are inscribed *chün* (lord, master) followed by an indecipherable character, presumably a personal name. It is significant for the advance of agriculture and the wealth of the farmer at this time that farming tools might be made of metal and by sophisticated methods. See also number 120.

120

Iron mould for casting socketed axes, consisting of two separate half-moulds and the core, excavated in 1953 at Hsing-lung, Hopei.

Length of the outer mould 28.6 cm, of the core 21.9 cm
Warring States : 5th–4th century BC

The procedure which allowed the Chinese caster to mould metal in metal is not properly understood. Nor is it clear what the metal of the product was. Bronze appears more likely than iron, having the lower melting point, but the possibility that iron was poured into an iron mould cannot be quite excluded, and is rather indicated by the fact that neither socketed axes of the kind implied here, nor sickle-blades produced in the mould number 119, have been found cast in bronze. With the ready manufacture of tools in iron these would be made cheaper to the craftsman than their bronze equivalents can ever have been. The socketed axe was already a very ancient Chinese implement (see the note on number 60).

120

121

121

Pottery bivalve mould for casting a tiger, excavated in 1959 at Hou-ma, Shansi.

Length 18 cm
Warring States : late 5th or 4th century BC

The many moulds excavated from the site of a bronze foundry at Hou-ma are proof that direct casting was still the main method even after lost-wax casting had been adopted for the most intricate work (compare number 135).

122

Clay model of the head of a monstrous tiger, excavated in 1959 at Hou-ma, Shansi.

Height 10.9 cm
Warring States : late 5th or 4th century BC

Positive models carved in clay were used for the manufacture of the negative moulds required for casting.

123

Clay relief model of a monster mask, excavated in 1959 at Hou-ma, Shansi.

Length 32.8 cm
Warring States : late 5th or 4th century BC

Like the preceding piece this model represents the initial stage of mould manufacture.

122

123

Period of the Warring States

475-221 BC

4

By the early fifth century BC all pretence at a feudal or federal state had to be abandoned. The pattern of power was now determined by systems of alliance which veered between the two policies of containing Ch'in by a north-south connexion of states, or containing Ch'u by an east-west line. Meanwhile the power of landowners and merchants increased. Draconian methods of administration and coercion of the peasantry led to increasing unrest. In armament the invention of the cross-bow and the long iron sword transformed strategy, and gradually iron ousted bronze as the material for common tools.

The artistic development is dominated by two new trends: first, the reduction of the old dragon schemes to bands or areas of continuous geometric ornament in which animal parts are hardly to be distinguished, as seen in the *tou* number 125; and, second, the adoption of new animal motifs which are akin to those used in the art of steppe nomads beyond the north-west frontier. The latter has been viewed as an influence of the nomad art upon China, but the flow was more probably in the other direction, from the northern Chinese zone outwards, for the new inventions are wholly in keeping with the enduring artistic methods of metropolitan China. The bird head of the *hu* number 124, the patterns numbers 122, 123, are instances of the new animal design. Tight spirals, comma-shaped hooks, bands of scales and a revived *t'ao-t'ieh* mask are its stock-in-trade. Dragons and snakes have a new lease of artistic life. Later, probably from the mid-third century BC, the ornamental schemes are further reduced to almost totally non-representational geometry, a development closely connected with the new technique of metallic inlay. This style flourished especially in the southern Ch'u kingdom, from whose noble tombs at Ch'angsha in Hunan and Chiang-ling in Hupei come some of the finest representative pieces. Ch'u artists worked in lacquer as well as bronze, and produced exuberant animal sculpture in wood.

126,127
130,131

128-130

(DW)

124

124

Bronze vase *hu*, with a lid shaped like the head of a bird of prey, excavated in 1970 at the Tsang-chia farm, Ma-chuang Commune, Chu-ch'eng, Shantung.

Height 47.5 cm
Warring States : late 4th or 3rd century BC

The *hu* was found with a group of bronze vessels and bells. It revives the idea of the ancient ritual *tsun* shaped like a bird, without copying any ancient piece exactly. The accompanying bells were nine in number and graded to sound a musical scale (compare numbers 102–110). The set of bronzes comprises the necessaries of ceremonial as these were conceived at the end of the Period of the Warring States. In addition to *hu* vases and bells it includes four *tou* tazzas, four *ting* tripods, and a goblet resembling the *ku* (see number 112).

125

Bronze pedestal vessel *tou*, inlaid with scrolled dragon motif in gold, excavated in 1965 at Ch'ang-chih, Shansi.

Height with lid 19.2 cm
Warring States : 5th or 4th century BC

The linear ornament of continuous figures descends in a tradition dating from about 600 BC, pioneered by artists whose work is best known from a hoard found at Li-yü, also in Shansi. The explicit animal masks included in earlier versions have here been reduced to the briefest allusion to a curl-snouted tiger, but the movement of the design remains similar. The geometric figure used in the band around the foot-rim is a detail quoted from the Li-yü scheme. *Tou* are frequent in pottery in the Period of the Warring States and probably served all the purposes of ceremony which at an earlier time required a variety of vessels. The lid inverted makes another bowl on a wide foot.

126

Vessel rim mount of bronze inlaid with silver, excavated in 1954 at Ho-chin, Shansi.

Diameter 12 cm
Warring States : late 4th or 3rd century BC

No bronze vessel is known to be fitted with such a rim' so it may be supposed that this mount was intended for a vessel of wood, probably lacquered. Even in the close spirals, where wire might be expected, the inlay is of silver foil cut in narrow strips.

127

Silver-inlaid bronze mount from a chariot, excavated in 1954 in Yung-chi, Shansi.

Length 21.3 cm
Warring States : late 4th or 3rd century BC

The function of such pieces is not precisely known. In chariot burials of this period the metal parts of the vehicles were mostly removed, so that the function of

124

125

bronze mounts found isolated is not always clear. This piece was probably fixed to the end of the shaft, possibly to support a strap connecting the traces or head-harness of the two horses. The ornament of this bronze and that of number 126 belongs to the later, geometricizing, phase of the Huai tradition.

128

Jade pendants cut in openwork in the shape of symmetrically paired dragons, excavated in 1965 from a tomb of the state of Ch'u at Chiang-ling, Hupei.

Length 26.4 cm
Warring States : 4th or early 3rd century BC

The art of jade carving was revived and developed in the late fifth and fourth centuries BC. Motifs akin to those

127

128 (DW)

129

cast in bronze were adapted to flat design, openwork of considerable difficulty evidently being made possible by an improved technique of sawing. Some of the detail argues the use of a rapid rotary drill. Double dragons were a common form of personal adornment which found its way into rich tombs. The brief spirals which fill the chief spaces of the figure continued in use in the earlier Han period, being often carved on a nipple to produce the 'grain pattern' (*ku wen*) of the antiquarians. The tomb at Chiang-ling evidently was the burial-place of a Ch'u nobleman, being in the vicinity of Ying, the early capital of the Ch'u state.

129

Bronze sword with variegated surface, excavated in 1965 from a tomb of the state of Ch'u at Chiang-ling, Hupei.

Length 60.8 cm
Warring States: 4th or early 3rd century BC

The form of grip, guard and blade profile are typical of the classical bronze sword made in China from the fifth to the third century BC. How the rhomboid design on the blade (the 'water-chestnut pattern' of the Chinese) was made on the metal surface is not yet understood. A great variety of these patterns is known, on swords, spearheads and occasionally on halberd blades. A number of the swords have in addition gold-inlaid inscriptions in bird-script (see number 167) calling them the weapons of the King of Yüeh, the state which dominated the central east coast of China after its conquest of Wu in 473 BC until its own defeat by Ch'u in 334 BC. Surprisingly, weapons of variegated bronze appear to be confined to the Ch'u region proper, in the modern territories of Hupei and Hunan. Thus the inscriptions may only mean that the swords are richly decorated like swords of Yüeh kings. If the meaning was more particular in the case of an inscribed sword found in the same tomb as the exhibited piece, we should take it to be a gift from a latter-day king of Yüeh to the person buried at Chiang-ling.

131A

130 A

130

130

Silver-inlaid wine vessel excavated in 1965 from a tomb of the state of Ch'u at Chiang-ling, Hupei.

Height 17.1 cm
Warring States: 4th or early 3rd century BC

The scrolled and geometricising ornament of the so-called Huai style, known in all the Ch'u territories, in its later phase produced design of symmetrical tendency consisting of more or less separated units. This development went hand in hand with the practice of inlay. Design cut to a shallow depth in the bronze and slightly undercut at the edge, was filled with beaten silver or gold foil. There is no finer example of such work than this wine receptacle. The interplay of angular and curved line and the spiral filling of the wider bands are characteristic.

131

131

Iron belt-hook inlaid with gold, excavated in 1963 from a tomb of the state of Ch'u at Chiang-ling, Hupei.

Length 46.3 cm
Warring States : 4th or early 3rd century BC

Inlay on iron in the Ch'u period was always of gold, the designs conforming to the prevalent Huai style. Accoutrements of sword and belt were evidently a permissible ostentation, and belt-hooks might be increased well beyond the practical size.

132

132–134

Pottery tiles excavated in 1966, 1964 and 1958 at Yi-hsien, Hopei.

Length 54.5 cm, 33.5 cm ; diameter 28 cm
Warring States : 5th–4th century BC

Ceramic tiles seem to be found, at the earliest, on sites of the Warring States Period, and are absent from the remains of habitations dating to the Shang dynasty and the Western Chou dynasty. It appears therefore that roofing with overlapping semi-cylindrical tiles was a comparatively late invention in China, coinciding approximately with the introduction of overlapping tiles in Greece. The specimens exhibited are joint-covering tiles. Number 132 is from the middle of a row, having rabbeted edges at the ends, and decorated with moulded triangular designs recalling the *t'ao-t'ieh*. Numbers 133 and 134 are terminal tiles from the eaves, decorated by vertical frontons with ornament elaborated from the same motif. Before such tiles came into use it is supposed that even noble buildings were roofed with thatch or shingles as humbler buildings continued to be.

134 (DW)

135 (DW)

135

Bronze monster mask and ring *p'u shou*, excavated in 1966 at Yi-hsien, Hopei.

Length of the mask 45.5 cm, diameter of the ring 29 cm
Warring States : 5th century BC

A monster mask set over a loose-hanging ring is found on bronze vessels (for an ancient example see the *lei* number 95) and in the Period of the Warring States was fixed on wooden outer coffins (*kuo*) and no doubt also on palace doors etc. The specimen exhibited is the finest and largest of such *p'u shou* ever discovered. It displays to perfection the compact composition of writhing animals and scrolled figures abstracted from them which is the burden of all decorative design from the fifth to the third century BC. In the late sixth century the *t'ao-t'ieh* monster-mask reappears, probably revived as a deliberate archaism, in allusion to the Shang ritual and artistic legacy. Here it is combined with a phoenix and a fully formed dragon distinct from the ancient *k'uei*. The casting can only have been by the lost-wax method, for which unambiguous evidence is still lacking from earlier time in China, although elsewhere it is the regular technique of bronze-age casters.

The victory of Ch'in and the consequent unification of China initiated a short period of despotic rule by a boastful monarch, who gave no thought to the patronage of art or of any but the most practical science. His armies campaigned into Annam (North Vietnam) and Korea, and in the north-west were engaged in continual struggle with the Hsiung-nu. Shih Huang Ti, 'First emperor' as he immodestly named himself, opposed the increasing power of merchants, controlled weights and measures (inscribing on many bronzes the text of his decree, a variant fragment of which is seen on the exhibit number 137) and built roads. His tomb is one of the most imposing of the imperial mounds, rising to a height of 43 metres, and surrounded by a double rectangular enclosure, the outer of which measures 2173 metres from north to south and 974 metres from east to west. According to Ssǔ-ma Ch'ien writing about a century after Shih Huang Ti's death, the tomb mound covers a subterranean palace, which contained among other treasures a model representing the 'hundred rivers' of the empire with mercury, and the 'vast sea'. The emperor's childless wives were killed and buried with him and all the workmen who had been employed in constructing the tomb were closed in it when it was sealed. Bushes and trees were planted on the mound to give it the appearance of a natural mountain. This grandiose tomb was plundered on Shih Huang Ti's defeat. It has not been excavated in modern times: the figure number 136 comes from one of the outer works of the precinct.

Under the following Western Han dynasty the intellectual release effected by the removal of Shih Huang Ti's oppression of theoretical dis-

cussion and writing led to a burst of creative scholarship. Texts were edited and historical documents scanned in an effort to reach an objective assessment of tradition in all its aspects. On the one hand Confucian philosophy was gradually rescued from its recent retreat and began to infiltrate the ranks of the official class. On the other, attention to popular superstitions and mythology became respectable among the educated. Mythology was hardly to be distinguished from theories of the structure of the universe to which astronomer-astrologers made a contribution from their objective observations. From the start the Chinese map of the heavens was based upon the polar axis and the celestial equator, and not upon the sun's course and the ecliptic, as so long was the practice in the West. The stories of mythical emperors and culture-heroes were collected. The cosmology of shaman ism is present in the idea of a central heaven-supporting pillar along which spirits could pass between this world and the spirit world. According to a Chinese myth the flood-hero Kung Kung, disputing the empire with Chuan Hsiu, ran his head against the pillar and bent it, so causing the stars to move from east to west and rivers to flow from west to east.

Ideas of this order entered Chinese art in the second century BC, as seen in the cosmic mountain of the censers called *po-shan-lu,* and the ubiquitous 'cloud scroll' of Han ornament which alludes to cosmic space through which immortals move. Schemes used to decorate bronze mirrors represent the square earth with its central mountain set in the round of heaven, or suggest the regular movements of the heavenly bodies. These motifs

are particularly frequent on objects produced in workshops established by government or under government patronage, in which such things as bronze mirrors and elaborately painted lacquer toilet boxes and wine cups were produced in great numbers for use as official gifts, both within China and in the newly acquired territories on the north-west and north-east frontiers.

During the second century BC Han art drew largely on the late style of the Period of the Warring States, and official and court patronage which was so largely responsible for change had conservative and archaistic leanings. We are fortunate in possessing the treasure of the Man-ch'eng tombs to illustrate the condition of art at the junction between this earliest Han phase and the innovation which occurred in the first century BC. The tombs of the prince Liu Sheng (a member of the imperial family enfeoffed at Chung-shan, posthumously called Ching) and his consort the princess Tou Wan are situated together about 150 kilometres south-west of Peking, in the side of a low hill in which two chambers were cut to a depth of fifty metres into the rock. More than 2800 objects were recovered in the excavation carried out in 1968, and these add immeasurably to our knowledge of the art of Western Han. At the turn of the second and first centuries BC the cosmic symbolism mentioned above has not yet entered decorative art, but the realism which was to characterize much of the art of the later Western Han period is already present. It is seen for example in the lamp shaped like a ram, and in the figures of leopards, all found in the Man-ch'eng tombs. It appears in fuller measure in pottery figures of horses and riders found in Shensi.

136

136

Pottery figure of a seated woman, found in 1964 at Lin-t'ung, Shensi.

Height 64.5 cm
Ch'in dynasty : 221–207 BC

The figure was found by workers in a cotton field near the burial mound of Ch'in Shih Huang Ti, the first emperor of united China. It had been buried about one metre underground and probably belonged to an offering sanctuary placed at the approaches of the imperial tomb and furnished with statues of servitors. The figure is individually modelled, not moulded like many smaller funeral figurines. The body is hollow and the head and arms made separately. In 1932 a similar figure was found also buried one metre below the surface, at a distance of twenty metres from the imperial mound. The custom of burying clay figures at the boundaries of great tombs has not previously been observed in China. In Japan this was done (the pottery *haniwa*) in the period corresponding to the first five centuries of the Christian era, possibly in imitation of a Chinese custom. The *haniwa*, representing warriors and servitors, were buried at intervals along the skirts of the mound.

137

Pottery measure with impressed inscription, excavated in 1963 at Tsou-hsien, Shantung.

Height 9.4 cm, diameter 20.5 cm
Ch'in dynasty : 221–207 BC

One of the unifying decrees promulgated by the founder of the Ch'in dynasty aimed at standardizing weights and measures. The inscription on this piece reads :
> As soon as his title was promulgated the emperor issued a decree to his ministers for regulating discrepancies in laws and in weights and measures. Where doubt existed he established a clear single standard. In the twenty-sixth year of his reign the empire is united and the feudal princes and the black-haired people enjoy peace.

138

Brick with impressed figures of mounted huntsmen and running animals, excavated in 1957 at Lin-t'ung, Shensi.

Length 47.5 cm
Ch'in dynasty : 221–207 BC

A scene of huntsmen and their prey set in a conventional landscape is a favourite motif in the decorative art of the Ch'in and Western Han dynasties. The fleeing deer are shown in the unreal position of the so-called 'flying gallop', a convention which was often used also for the horse. In this case the horse's legs are shown differently, but their position is still not one seen in real movement, as modern cinematography proves. The huntsmen have short compound bows with a triple curve.

139

Jade funeral suit of the princess Tou Wan, wife of the

137A

138 (detail)

139A

The jade suit in the condition in which it was discovered

139 (DW)

prince Liu Sheng enfeoffed at Chung-shan, found in 1968 in her tomb at Man-ch'eng, Hopei.

Length 172 cm
Western Han dynasty : late 2nd century BC

Preoccupied with the search for an elixir of life, Taoist magicians received increasing notice in the Western Han period. Their lore included a belief that jade could prevent the decay of the corpse, which therefore from about the time of the Man-ch'eng tombs was often furnished with small jade pieces intended to stop the nine orifices of the body, a cicada of jade being laid upon the tongue. Prince Liu and his wife took this belief to ostentatious length and prepared for themselves complete suits of jade, being perhaps the instigators of a fashion which was still observed occasionally in later times. Lady Tou's suit consists of 2,160 tablets of jade, varying in size from 4.5 x 3.5 cm to 1.5 x 1 cm, and 0.2 to 0.35 cm in thickness. The suit divides into twelve parts (back and front of torso and head, arms, legs, gloves and shoes) made as separate units with piping of silk-wound iron wire along the edges. The remaining stitching is with gold wire (of which in all 700 grammes were used), passed through holes at the corners of the tablets, except across the chest, where the jade tablets are held in place by adhesive attaching their binding tapes to a heavy cloth lining. The decayed tapes have had to be replaced. The jade was probably imported from Sinkiang.

Colour plate.

140

Pillow of gilded bronze inlaid with jade, found in 1968 in the tomb of the princess Tou Wan at Man-ch'eng, Hopei.

Length 41.3 cm
Western Han dynasty : late 2nd century BC

The pillow has ends shaped like deer-heads. The custom of using animal figures, generally lions, as supports for funeral pillows recurs in the Sung period, when the pillows are made of porcelain.

140

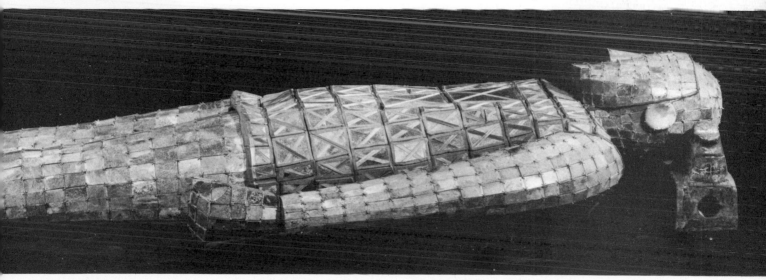

141, 142

Two jade tablets *huang*, found in 1968 in the tomb of the princess Tou Wan at Man-ch'eng, Hopei.

Length 13 cm and 13.7 cm
Western Han dynasty : late 2nd century BC

The custom of placing the crescentic jade tablet called *huang* in close contact with the dead was revived in the fourth century BC. These pieces have decoration similar to that which appears on *pi*, and may have been made from fragments of these rings (see numbers 143–148).

143–148

Six jade rings *pi*, found in 1968 in the tomb of the princess Tou Wan at Man-ch'eng, Hopei.

Diameters from 14.1 cm to 21.2 cm
Western Han dynasty : late 2nd century BC

From the neolithic period onwards jade rings appear to have had symbolic meaning associating them with burial and the afterworld, although no early explanation of them has survived. In the third century BC the compilers of ritual texts, who drew on ancient materials, describe the *pi* as a symbol of the sky appropriate for the emperor's use in performing the sacrifice to heaven. In burials of the Period of the Warring States *pi* are found placed, for example, at either side of the head and under each knee of the corpse. According to the *Chou li* there were six jades (*kuei, chang, pi, tsung, hu, huang*) due to be placed in the coffin of a member of the imperial house. In the present instance only the third and the last of these were so placed. There is no record of a burial which contained all the ritual jades in their assigned places. Compare numbers 51 and 141-142.

149

Reproduction *of a bronze seal found in the tomb of the princess Tou Wan at Man-ch'eng, Hopei.*

Side 2 cm, thickness 0.7 cm
Late 2nd century BC

One side of the seal reads: Tou Wan; and the other: The Lady Tou, Hsü. The last is an informal personal name. In the tomb was found also an impression on clay from another seal which reads Chung-shan tz'ŭ-ssŭ, *i.e. Superintendent of ancestral shrines at Chung-shan. A change made in this title in 104 BC suggests that the princess died before that year.*

150, 151

Two parcel-gilt bronze figures of leopards inlaid with silver and garnets, found in 1968 in the tomb of the princess Tou Wan at Man-ch'eng, Hopei.

Height 3.5 cm
Western Han dynasty : late 2nd century BC

These are two of a set of four bronze leopards which probably performed the same service in the burial as the commoner summary jade carvings of pig-like animals

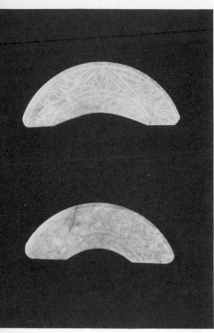

141,142

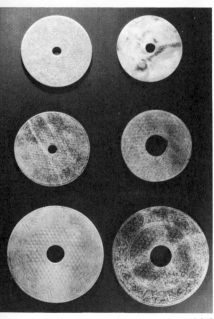

143-148

149

150,151 (DW)

which were used to weigh down the sleeves and edges of funeral palls. The exquisite workmanship of these pieces would be hard to match in any other product of the Han craftsman.

Colour plate.

152, 153

Two feet from a bronze vessel representing bears rearing over birds, found in 1968 in the tomb of the princess Tou Wan at Man-ch'eng, Hopei.

Height 11.1 cm, 11.7 cm
Western Han dynasty : late 2nd century BC

Feet in the shape of bears are a common feature of Han bronze vessels from the first century BC onwards. The examples from the Man-ch'eng tomb differ from these in representing the bear rearing instead of standing with hunched shoulders, and in adding the birds. Bears figure in Han stories as a borrowing from northern myth, and relate distantly to the bear-cult of north-eastern Asia. In particular the genie Ch'ih-yu, shown as a bear brandishing weapons in all four paws, became a symbol of bravery and an army mascot (see numbers 169, 173, 175).

154

Grey pottery basin painted in white and red with birds, fish and clouds, found in 1968 in the tomb of the princess Tou Wan at Man-ch'eng, Hopei.

Height 14.7 cm, diameter 55.5 cm
Western Han dynasty : late 2nd century BC

The clouds and the design suggesting a symbolic scheme of planets and stars are in keeping with cosmic

152 (CG)

153 (CG)

154

themes introduced into decorative design in the first century BC, as are to be seen mainly on bronze mirrors. In this context the comparative naturalism of the fish and cranes is unusual.

155

Bronze censer in the shape of a cosmic mountain, *po-shan-lu*, held up by a man seated on a monster, found in 1968 in the tomb of the princess Tou Wan at Man-ch'eng, Hopei.

Height 32.4 cm
Western Han dynasty : late 2nd century BC

This invention of the Western Han period shows a craggy mountain rising from the sea, its slopes inhabited by men and wild animals. Around its base move from right to left, three of the Four Sacred Animals which at this time emerge in Han myth as symbols of the four quarters of heaven : the green dragon of the east, white tiger of the west, red bird of the south and dark warrior of the north. The last is omitted here, as often happens, for it was uncertain what form it should take : in spite of the name it comes to be represented by a snake encircling a tortoise.

156

Bronze tripod lamp on a tray, found in 1968 in the tomb of the princess Tou Wan, at Man-ch'eng, Hopei.

Height of the lamp 5.2 cm, diameter of the tray 22.1 cm
Western Han dynasty : late 2nd century BC

Two inscriptions on these pieces describe them as bronze dishes with handle from the palace store of Chung-shan, in one case prefixing 'imperial' and in both cases ending with a character *shuang*, which appears to be a storeman's mark or name.

157

Bronze bowl *chüan,* with mask-and-ring handles and inscribed, found in 1968 in the tomb of the princess Tou Wan at Man-ch'eng, Hopei.

Height 13 cm, diameter 28.1 cm
Western Han dynasty : late 2nd century BC

The bowl is of a common Western Han type, the handle descending from the *p'u shou* of the Period of the Warring States, as seen in number 135. The inscription reads :
> Palace store at Chung-shan one bronze *chüan*. Contents 3 *sheng*. Weight 7 *chin* 13 *liang*. No 59. 34th year 4th month. Bought by the *lang-chung* Ting at Ho-tung at the price of 840.

The date is equivalent to 107 BC. *Lang-chung* is the official name for a member of a personal staff. Ho-tung is a town at Hsia-hsien, Shansi. It is calculated that the price recorded (the sum is in the bronze coinage, *ch'ien*) would in the reign of Wu Ti be approximately the equivalent of something over 20 *tan* of grain, or sufficient to feed one person for a year, or a year and a half.

155 (CG)

156

157

157A

158

159

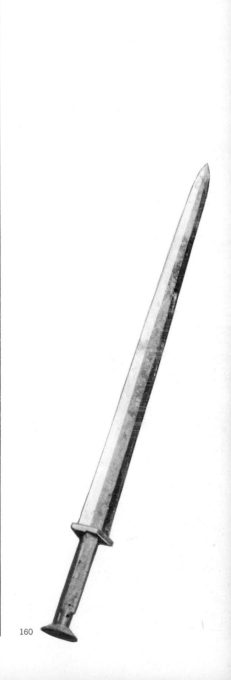

160

158

Single-edged iron dagger *hsiao,* with gold-bound hilt-ring, found in 1968 in the tomb of the prince Liu Sheng at Man-ch'eng, Hopei.

Length 25.7 cm
Western Han dynasty : late 2nd century BC, before 113 BC

When iron was first used for the manufacture of swords and daggers the shapes of existing bronze weapons were not copied, since these depended on casting, while iron was forged. The shape of this *hsiao* was reproduced exactly in larger size to serve as a sword, when it was sometimes made of bronze. Ornament is confined to the hilt-ring, here encased in gold. Swords of this kind were the main weapon of the large infantry armies which fought in the wars of the Period of the Warring States, and in particular won battles for the state of Ch'in.

159

Bronze dagger of the type *pi shou,* found in 1968 in the tomb of the prince Liu Sheng at Man-ch'eng, Hopei.

Length 28.1 cm
Western Han dynasty : late 2nd century BC, before 113 BC

This dagger with fully cast grip (i.e. not requiring a thick silk binding like the grips of the majority of bronze swords) and with only a slight guard was fashionable in metropolitan China in the Ch'in and Western Han periods. Earlier the *pi shou* type of dagger had been manufactured in the northern territories, in the vicinity of the Great Wall and was favoured by China's nomadic neighbours. Its use in China proper marks an influence of nomadic culture, which is seen also in decorative art of the Western Han. It was with such a weapon, bought for a hundred pieces of gold after a search for the 'sharpest *pi-shou*' in the empire, that the celebrated assassin Ching K'o, instigated by Tan the heir-apparent of the state of Yen, made his unsuccessful attempt on the life of the first Ch'in emperor.

160

Bronze sword found in 1968 in the tomb of the prince Liu Sheng at Man-ch'eng, Hopei.

Length 72.5 cm
Western Han dynasty : late 2nd century BC, before 113 BC

This is a late representative of the classical bronze sword manufactured in China from the fifth century BC. It is rare in Western Han, and in Eastern Han disappears altogether.

161

Gilded bronze halberd blade *ko,* with a shaft finial carrying the figure of a bird, found in 1968 in the tomb of the prince Liu Sheng at Man-ch'eng, Hopei.

Length 20 cm
Western Han dynasty : late 2nd century BC, before 113 BC

For the earlier history of the *ko* see number 59. It descends from Shang times. In this form and in the Western Han period it must rank as a parade weapon, for the iron sword and a modified iron version of the *ko*, in which it acquires also a bayonet-like point, has superseded the *ko* in warfare. The association of bird ornament with the *ko* is also traditional.

162, 163

Gold and silver needles for acupuncture and cautery, found in 1968 in the tomb of the prince Liu Sheng at Man-ch'eng, Hopei.

Length 6.5 cm, 7.1 cm
Western Han dynasty : late 2nd century BC, before 113 BC

The difference of shape and size may imply a difference of technique, but possibly both needles were used in the two treatments.

164

Bronze lamp in the shape of a seated ram, found in 1968 in the tomb of the prince Liu Sheng at Man-ch'eng, Hopei.

Height 18.6 cm, length 23 cm
Western Han dynasty : late 2nd century BC, before 113 BC

A new realism of animal form enters the art of the Western Han, particularly towards the end of the second

162

163

164 (DW)

century BC, and this piece may be seen as an early example of the style. On the shoulders it retains the outline of the scrolled figure which is placed in this position on animal designs of the Period of the Warring States. Raised on its hinge to rest on the head the ram's back forms an oil reservoir. The wick must then have hung over the edge of this bowl, so that the flame was over the hollow body.

165

165

Bronze lamp with shade and chimney, found in 1968 in the tomb of the prince Liu Sheng at Man-ch'eng, Hopei.

Height 32,8 cm
Western Han dynasty: late 2nd century BC, before 113 BC

By a somewhat impractical device the heat and smoke from the lamp wick are led into a tube which connects with the lower reservoir. The construction of the gilded bronze lamp inscribed 'long fidelity' which was found in the tomb of Liu Sheng's wife Tou Wan is similar, the smoke being led into the arm of the seated servant who holds the lamp.

166

Bronze vase *hu*, parcel-gilt with ornament of dragons in clouds, found in 1968 in the tomb of the prince Liu Sheng at Man-ch'eng, Hopei.

Height with lid 59 cm
Western Han dynasty: late 2nd century BC, before 113 BC

Gilding begins in China in the Period of the Warring States, when foil was occasionally burnished on to bronze, but it is not common before the first century BC, when fire-gilding was invented. In the latter process an amalgam of gold and mercury is painted on bronze, and then heat is applied to volatilize and disperse the mercury, leaving only gold covering the bronze surface. The Chinese craftsman was particularly skilled in parcel-gilding, confining the amalgam painting closely to the desired areas. The cloud scroll derived from the pre-Han tradition is specially characteristic of ornament of the second century BC, cloud and portions of dragons mingling inextricably in the design.

166

167

Bronze vase *hu*, inlaid in gold and silver with scrolled designs and characters of the decorative bird script, found in 1968 in the tomb of the prince Liu Sheng at Man-ch'eng, Hopei.

Height with lid 40 cm
Western Han dynasty: late 2nd century BC

The combination of angular and curving figures, in part symmetrically arranged, is inherited from the art of the Period of the Warring States, which in this form survived into the Western Han. The artificial elaboration of the 'bird' characters (so-called from the earlier form practised in Ch'u and Yüeh in which more legible birds are incorporated) preserves only a slender connexion

with script shapes. The inscription has been deciphered to read:

> May good fare fill your gate, expand your girth, extend your life, keep sickness at bay.

168

Bronze vase of square section, *fang,* with gold-inlaid ornament excavated in 1964 at Sian, Shensi.

Height 61 cm
Western Han dynasty: 1st century BC

The vase was found near a silver figurine of the 'winged men' who serve the Queen Mother of the West in the immortals' paradise in the western mountains. The latter belongs to Taoist myth entering art in the first century BC. If the vase belongs to this time it marks one of the latest survivals of the artistic legacy of the Period of the Warring States, showing the final geometricized version of the dragon scrolls, now reduced to wholly symmetrical figures.

168 (DW)

169

169

Gilt bronze wine bowl supported by three tigers, excavated in 1962 at Yu-yü, Shansi.

Height 34.7 cm, diameter 65.5 cm
Western Han dynasty: 26 BC

This and the wine warmer number 175 were found buried at the foot of an earth cliff, from the top of which they had apparently fallen in a collapse caused by water erosion. Although no tomb was traced, these bronzes and others accompanying them were probably grave-gifts of an official posted to Yu-yü, a garrison town situated near the Great Wall in north Shansi. The inscription engraved on the lip of the bowl reads: 'Bronze wine vessel (*chiu tsun*) weighing 120 *chin* made in Ho-p'ing 3rd year (i.e. 26 BC) by Hu Fu of Yin-ch'eng at Chü-yang'. Ying-ch'eng was near to the modern Ying-hsien, called Chü-yang in the inscription. On the sides below the handles are the lightly engraved figures of a deer, Bactrian camel, elephant, the bear genie Ch'ih-yu (compare numbers 152–3, 173, 175), rhinoceros and tiger, and below the lip, tiger and deer, all in lively graphic style. The areas of the figures now appear silvery, the effect either of silvering with amalgam (a difficult process) or of tinning. Originally the outlines and inner detail of the animals were painted in black, white and red, of which only traces remain. Ronde-bosse tigers replace the more usual bears as feet.

170

Pottery vase *hu,* decorated in unfired colours, excavated at Loyang, Honan.

Height 43.2 cm
Western Han dynasty: 2nd or 1st century BC

The decoration of pottery with unfired pigments begins in the late fourth century BC, the intention then being the same as in the present exhibit: to imitate to some extent the ornament normally applied to bronze vessels. The

170 (DW)

171

172

173A

173B

173C
173D

usual *t'ao-t'ieh* monster masks are moulded on the sides of this pot, but ring-handles are lacking.

Colour plate.

171, 172

Pottery figures of horses and riders excavated in 1965 at Hsien-yang, Shensi.

Height 65 cm, 68.5 cm
Western Han dynasty: 1st century BC

When Chang Ch'ien was sent by the emperor Wu Ti on a mission to the far west which brought him in 128 BC to Sogdiana and Ferghana, between the Oxus and the Jaxartes, he reported on fine horses bred there, the like of which the Chinese had never seen. It was not until they defeated the prince of the Ta-yüan in Ferghana in 101 BC that the Chinese succeeding in acquiring some of these animals. During the following century the new breed was introduced into China with great success and the 'celestial' 'blood-sweating' horses became famous. For draught and riding these were incomparably better than earlier breeds known in China, all of which were related to the Przewalski horse of the steppes, and were seldom above thirteen hands. The prestige of the western horses made them the status symbol of rich and official families, and as such they were portrayed in figurines placed with the dead. The conventions of anatomy and stance used here are to be compared with those seen in the bronze horses from Kansu (numbers 206 ff and 222) which are at least one century later in date. The Hsien-yang horses make a revealing contrast with the life-size stone horses placed outside the tomb of Wu Ti's general Ho Ch'ü-ping (died 117 BC), which copy the steppe breed in a powerful naive style unrelated to the convention adopted shortly afterwards for the new breed. The horses bred today in Kabardia in the north Caucasus probably descend from the ancient Ferghana stock. By their narrow chest, sinewy build and long legs they resemble the western horses of Han China.

173

Bronze tube inlaid in gold and silver with figures of men and animals in landscape, excavated in 1965 at Ting-hsien in Hopei.

Length 26.5 cm
Western Han dynasty: 1st century BC

Free inlay-work closely imitating painting was an invention of the Chinese craftsman towards the end of the second century BC. A *po-shan-lu* ('mountain-shaped censer') from the tomb of the prince Liu Sheng at Man-ch'eng in Hopei is the earliest dated example of the distinctive Han inlay style, belonging probably to the decade before 113 BC. The work of the present exhibit is more advanced, displaying in gold and silver, in precise miniature, mountain sides crowded with animals rushing and posturing among trees and crags. The subjects include tiger, boar, birds in profusion, mountain bear and the bear Ch'ih-yu (see number 152–3), a large phoenix, and an elephant with mahout and two passengers. The tube was possibly a chariot ornament.

174 (DW)

174

Bronze vessel in the shape of an unreal animal, *hsi tsun*, excavated in 1965 at Lien-shui, Kiangsu.

Height 41.8 cm
Western Han dynasty : 2nd century BC

An animal something like a tapir was first adopted as the shape of a bronze ritual vessel at Li-yu in Shansi in the sixth century BC. Such *hsi tsun* were made sporadically afterwards, and in the Western Han period were changed to resemble more closely a water buffalo. This piece is in the older tradition, and its scrolled and geometricized ornament belongs to the style of the last pre-Han centuries rather than to the art of Western Han. In this respect it shows the archaism of official art in the second century BC.

175

Gilt bronze wine warmer supported on three bears, excavated in 1962 at Yu-yü, Shansi.

Height 24.5 cm, diameter 23.4 cm
Western Han dynasty : 26 BC

The inscription engraved near the lip reads: 'Bronze vessel for warming wine (*wen chiu tsun*) weighing 24 *chin* made by Hu Fu of Chung-ling in Ho-p'ing 3rd year' (26 BC). In scenes of feasting which belong to this period, carved in stone or impressed on bricks, the *tsun* is shown standing on the floor between rows of guests. This is the first time that its purpose is named in an inscription. Canisters of this shape made of lacquer also held cosmetics etc. Hu Fu here describes himself as resident at Yu-yü (ancient Chung-ling), while on another bronze which he signs (number 169) he is at Ying-hsien. The two places are only a short distance apart. The ornament, here exceptionally raised in relief, is the familiar one of tigers and dragons in procession (on the lid) and the rocky landscape of animals: deer, camel, tiger, birds (on the sides). The latter group includes the dancing bear Ch'ih-yu, which stood for courage (see numbers 152–3, 169, 173). Number 169 comes from the same site.

175

(*w*)

The Han dynasty historian Ssŭ-ma Chien records a story of the origin of the Tien kingdom of Yünnan which is probably a dynastic fiction, intended to legitimate Tien rulers by connecting them with Chinese princes. A general of the Chinese state of Ch'u, Chuang Ch'iao, descended from a king, is said to have conquered the Tien territory in a campaign between 339 and 329 BC. Then finding his return barred by an advance of the Ch'in army across his route, Chuang Ch'iao settled in Tien as its king, and his men became progenitors of a people which inherited Chinese culture. Some bronzes obtained in a Kunming shop in 1946 by Dr Fraser of the Scottish Mission to Lepers were the first indication of a culture distinct from the main Chinese tradition and of high attainment. Complete excavation of the burial ground of Tien nobles on Shih-chai-shan hill near Kunming was undertaken in 1955-60; it has provided a picture of the life, warfare and art of a barbarian client nation of China with a completeness unmatched in any other of the neighbouring territories. After the submission to China in 109 BC, Chinese imports reached Tien, and these were found in the tombs together with bronze vessels, figures and weapons of untypical design and quite original artistic style. Some halberd blades and battle-axes appear to be derived from Chinese prototypes of much earlier date. Tomb number 6 contained a gold seal inscribed 'King of Tien', a token of office awarded by the Chinese emperor. Particular interest attaches to the drum-shaped vessels used as containers for cowries, for they strongly support the argument that the Tien culture is at the origin of the so-called Dong-son bronze tradition far spread in South-east Asia.

176

176 (DW)

176 (two details)

177 (DW)

178

179

176

Bronze cowrie container decorated with peacocks and human figures in the round, excavated in 1955–60 from tomb number 1 at Shih-chai-shan, Yünnan.

Total height 27.5 cm, diameter of base 30.9 cm
2nd or early 1st century BC

The figures are set on top of vessels which were buried full of cowries (a form of currency). The shapes of the vessels reproduce those of bronze drums, one type of which is found dispersed over much of south-east Asia and Java. The variety of drum shapes at Shih-chai-shan suggests that the manufacture and the ritual employment of the drums originated in Yünnan and among the Tien people. The largest figure, an important female, is receiving offerings. Her coiffure does not conform to the hour-glass shape which is seen on other Tien women represented in bronze. The people around her hold trays with their gifts (some offer fruit, and one a large fish), or are seated on the ground engaged in weaving at a simple loom whose warp threads are stretched between a bar fixed at the waist and another held by the feet.

177

Bronze duck with snakes, excavated in 1955–60 from tomb number 20 at Shih-chai-shan, Yünnan.

Height 11.2 cm
Western Han dynasty : 2nd or early 1st century BC

The duck resembles the *yüan-yang* (mandarin) variety.

Colour plate.

178

Bronze figure of a standing deer excavated in 1955–60 from tomb number 5 at Shih-chai-shan, Yünnan.

Height 15.6 cm
Western Han dynasty : 2nd or early 1st century BC

The preoccupation with animals in general, and a predilection for scenes of animal combat and for the deer are all traits which ally the art of Tien to that of the nomads of Central Asia. But the two styles differ considerably, that of Tien showing much greater skill in depicting three-dimensional form, and less interest in formal abstraction of shapes and fantastic combinations.

179

Bronze figure of a peacock found excavated in 1955–60 from tomb number 17 at Shih-chai-shan, Yünnan.

Height 14.4 cm
Western Han dynasty : 2nd or early 1st century BC

Although less frequent than the bull, deer and snake, the peacock appears to play an important role in Tien myth. It is also associated with the drums (compare number 176, where peacocks are attached at the sides between the handles of the vessel).

180

Bronze ploughshare from excavations in 1955–60 at Shih-chai-shan, Yünnan.

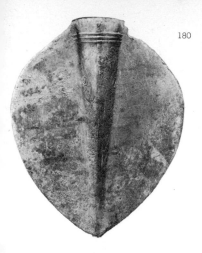

180

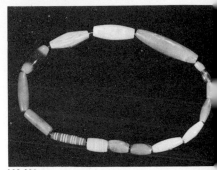

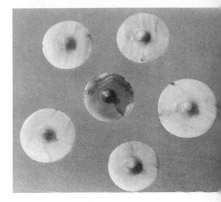

182-203

Length 30 cm
Western Han dynasty: 2nd or early 1st century BC

The bronze ploughshare buried with the Tien kings and chieftains, sometimes as many as five in a grave, probably were used in ritual ploughing.

181

Shaft-hole battle axe of bronze decorated with free-standing ducks and snakes, excavated in 1955–60 from tomb number 13 at Shih-chai-shan, Yünnan.

Height 24 cm
Western Han dynasty: 2nd or early 1st century BC

This axe form is descended from a similar weapon made in north China in the late Shang period. The ground line of the composition is provided by snakes. Chinese writers record that the snake was taken as an emblem by some tribes in south China.

182–203

Agate beads and rondels excavated in 1955–60 from tomb number 13 at Shih-chai-shan, Yünnan.

Beads: length 1.1 cm to 7.3 cm
Rondels: diameter 4.4 cm to 5.8 cm
Western Han dynasty: 2nd or early 1st century BC

In recent times agate has come to China from Java, Borneo, Sumatra and Malaya. The Tien agate may also have been imported from a distance.

204

Bronze ornament of bocranium, bulls and snakes, excavated in 1955–60 from tomb number 13 at Shih-chai-shan, Yünnan.

Width 11.2 cm
Western Han dynasty: 2nd or early 1st century BC

As semi nomadic stock raisers who according to the Han historian Ssǔ-ma Ch'ien 'followed their herds about', the people of Tien were accustomed to offer their cattle in sacrifice, as may be seen in the ritual procession depicted in one of their bronzes. Ornaments of the kind represented by this exhibit probably commemorate the rite on which the fertility of their herds was believed to depend. The realism of the bull heads and the indifference to the incongruity of scale are characteristic traits, and in all such compositions snakes were indispensable.

205

Bronze figures of two tigers and a boar in combat excavated in 1955–60 from tomb number 3 at Shih-chai-shan, Yünnan.

Length 17.1 cm.
Western Han dynasty: 2nd or early 1st century BC

The figures are in high relief, the plain back of the composition showing that it was meant to be fastened to a surface.

181

204

205 (DW)

The prosperity of China under the house of Han, restored after the brief interregnum of Wang Mang, is reflected in the abundant goods buried with men of official rank, representatives of a landowning class that was now all-powerful. The break with the ancient tradition of non-realistic, formalizing art occurred about the middle of the first century BC. Verisimilitude then counted seriously in painting and sculpture for the first time. The *Notice of Famous Painters of Successive Dynasties* (by Chang Yen-yüan of the early ninth century AD) lists painters commissioned at the court from 43 BC onwards, a dozen names being recorded for the two Han dynasties. The famous mural reliefs of the Wu Liang tombs in Shantung depict scenes of exemplary filial piety and incidents from the life of Confucius, but also real events of comparatively recent history, and the style reflects that of contemporary painting. Pottery figurines and models now frequently placed in tombs witness to the same interest in perpetuating the objects and scenes of everyday life. Figures of soldiers, servants, acrobats and such genies as the evil-averting Fang-hsiang (see numbers 297,298), models of houses, whole farmsteads, pigsties, potters' workshops and rice-pounding trip-hammers (to name a few of the subjects) are made in a style always fresh, full of observation and often witty. Jade was still carved in the style inherited from the pre-Han period, although this craft was now in decline. Genre subjects of a kind that under the Western Han were to be found only in the art of the Tien barbarians, are now the stock-in-trade of the metropolitan craftsman. An important theme was the horse, of which the most original interpretation that has been found is seen in the bronze figurines of the Wu-wei tomb excavated in 1969 in Kansu. This burial was accompanied by 177 bronze objects which still remained after two robberies in antiquity. It was discovered and reported by members of the Hsin-hsien commune.

Under the Eastern Han, bronze work of the traditional kind in massive ornamental vessels or fine inlay of silver and gold was seldom executed (such pieces as the *hu* number 168, the bowl number 169, and the animated animal parades of the censers and caskets, like that on number 175, belong to a final flowering of the Western Han). Instead the bronze-caster's artistry is lavished on mirrors, though his inventions follow more in the wake of the simpler designs of the first century BC than the dragon-cum-cloud conventions of the previous century. In the late second century AD the finest mirrors were cast in the district of Shao-hsing in Kiangsu. They present gods and men, horses and carriages, in realistic relief of a new kind. The scenes relate mostly to the myth of Hsi Wang Mu, the 'Queen Mother of the West', and the paradise in the Western Mountains where she presided over immortals, attended by Winged Men, *yü jen*. In Kiangsu this iconography was to persist into the third century. The tales of immortals were part of the Taoist lore, which was taken seriously by the educated, much as the contemporary Romans dabbled in the Egyptian mysteries, similarly preoccupied with spirits and the after-life.

The most notable technical advance of the Eastern Han period which can be documented archaeologically is the development of ceramic glaze. Both the feldspathic and the lead-fluxed varieties have a pre-Han history, but it was not until the end of the first century BC, and particularly in the first century AD that a form of green hard glaze was moderately refined, furnishing the point of departure for the later cycle of Yüeh ware in Chekiang and Kiangsu. Simultaneously green and brown lead glazes were perfected in Honan, Shensi and Shantung, and used to coat many of the pottery models previously mentioned. When the pottery imitated a bronze vessel, which was frequent in the grave goods, the green glaze suggested patinated bronze. The antiquarian spirit was already abroad.

288
229-234

226,227

206-222

235

206, 207

Bronze figures of pawing and neighing horses excavated in 1969 at Wu-wei, Kansu.

Height 36.5 cm, 38 cm
Eastern Han dynasty : 2nd century AD

Colour plate.

208, 209, 210

Three bronze figures of horsemen one unarmed, one holding a spear and one holding a *chi* halberd, excavated in 1969 at Wu-wei, Kansu.

Total height 39 cm, 52.3 cm, 53 cm
Eastern Han dynasty : 2nd century AD

Probably the models were furnished originally with harness of perishable material. All the horsemen wear leggings, and ride without stirrups, which evidently had not yet been brought into use in China or in Central Asia. The *chi* is a combination of spearhead with the traditional *ko* halberd, now made in iron, which was a regular infantry and cavalry arm in the Eastern Han. The head of the fiery horse is shown checked by the curb.

211–221

Bronze models of horse carriages, drivers and attendants excavated in 1969 at Wu-wei, Kansu.

Height of horses 40 cm, 40 cm, 38 cm ; of carriages 33 cm, 43.5 cm ; length of third carriage 63 cm
Eastern Han dynasty : 2nd century AD

As in the Period of the Warring States the power of a state was reckoned by the number of chariots it possessed, so the rank of an official of the Eastern Han might be seen from the number of carriages in his train, and models of them were buried with him, or painted on the walls of his tomb. In the second century AD, Chinese carriage harness reached a point of efficiency only inferior to the hard collar of modern harness. From the Shang dynasty until the fourth century BC the harness employed a hard yoke and throat-and-girth straps, the combined effect of which was to choke the animal as it

206 (DW)   207 (DW)   208

209   210

pulled. But the breast-strap harness of the later Han period allowed the draught to be exerted from the horse's chest, without any tendency to strangling, and a great increase in the force exerted. This improvement owed much to the fact that the traces are attached to the middle of the shafts, the ends of which fork and rise to two positions to hold yokes on the back and against the withers. Often there is no girth. By means of this harness one horse could draw a carriage holding several persons. The upward bend of the shafts was essential: the third carriage exhibited has gently curving shafts which imply a different method of harnessing, perhaps for lighter loads. The hard collar, in China as in Europe, was a discovery of the later Middle Ages.

The drivers of the carriages sit behind a wide dashboard. The umbrella and the axe are signs of authority. The hands of the standing men probably held reins attached to the head harness. The sculptural style is that of the flying horse (number 222), and superior to that of pottery horses of a century earlier (compare numbers 171 and 172). An example of the inscriptions engraved on some of the figures is:

> The governor Chang Yeh-ch'ang and His Lordship's son Ana: one saddle horse and one horse-leading slave.

Seals found in the tomb give the title 'general', by whom Governor Chang is no doubt meant, although the names are illegible.

222

Bronze figure of a flying horse standing by one leg on a swallow, excavated in 1969 at Wu wei, Kansu.

Height 34.5 cm, length 45 cm
Eastern Han dynasty: 2nd century AD

Horses of the tall western breed — 'celestial horses' — were well known in China by the later Han period, having been introduced from Sogdiana at the beginning of the first century BC (see numbers 171 and 172). This piece is the most remarkable sculpture of such a horse that has been found, and the only one which seriously attempts to represent the posture of the galloping animal. The position of the legs, while not accurate, is nearer to reality than that adopted in the convention of the 'flying gallop' (compare numbers 108 and 292). The

(CG)

222 (DW)

222 (DW)

figure balances on the swallow, the bird turning its head in surprise at the touch of the hoof: perhaps a chance encounter rather than a journey on the bird's back, so we may speak of a flying horse. *Fei yen*, 'flying swallow' was a sobriquet of the lady Chao, wife of the emperor Ch'eng Ti at the end of the first century BC, given for her skill in dancing. Earlier the emperor Wen Ti possessed nine fine horses of which one bore the same name, although in his time the horses can hardly have been of the western breed. The modelling of the head of the flying horse recalls that of a jade carving which belongs to the same period. The horse is neighing, with an apt tilt of the head.

Colour plate.

223

Procession of horsemen and carriages, *hand-copied from a wall painting in a tomb investigated in 1971 at An-p'ing, Hopei.*

Length 327 cm
Eastern Han dynasty : 2nd century AD

A constant theme in the decoration of rich tombs of the Eastern Han period is the cortège of an official making a progress through the territory of his jurisdiction. The chief carriage, not always to be identified, is towards the middle of the train. In other examples (painted or in bas-relief) where the subordinate officials are named in inscriptions they prove to be ushers, inspectors, keepers of accounts etc.

224

Wooden carving of a monkey excavated in 1959 at Wu-wei, Kansu

Height 32.5 cm
Eastern Han dynasty : 1st or 2nd century AD

Wood rarely survives in the soil of north China and knowledge of Han sculpture in this medium is slight. A series of figures of strange deities is known from tombs at Ch'ang-sha, in Hunan, in which the broad treatment of relief resembles that of the exhibited piece. This style contrasts with the full modelling seen in pottery figurines of this period (compare numbers 171 and 172). Kansu and Hunan lie outside the metropolitan area of Honan and the north-east in which much of typical Han style originated.

225

Wooden carving of a unicorn charging, excavated in 1959 at Wu-wei, Kansu.

Height 38.5 cm, total length 59 cm
Eastern Han dynasty : 1st or 2nd century AD

The Chinese unicorn, *ch'i-lin* was anciently described as having the body of a deer, the tail of a cow and the hoofs of a horse. From the Han period it was believed to be a benevolent animal, whose fleshy horn equips it for war, although it never does harm. Its appearance in the empire was a good portent, deserving immediate report

224

225 (CG)

223

to the emperor. *Ch'i-lin* was used metaphorically of a great genius, especially a statesman, and it was taken as a symbol of success in the scholar's and official's career. A connexion with the unicorn of western heraldry has been suspected, despite the bodily difference, but this cannot be closely demonstrated.

226, 227

Two rings of light green jade, *pi*, excavated in 1969 and 1959 at Ting-hsien, Hopei.

Total height 30 cm, 25.5 cm
Eastern Han dynasty: 1st or 2nd century AD

The history and symbolic function of the *pi* is mentioned under number 50. These pieces are to be seen as archaistic allusion to the Huai style of the Period of the Warring States. In each case the treatment of the openwork reveals its Han date: the dragons symmetrically supporting a ring is a new motif, anticipating the two dragons in pursuit of a flaming pearl which enter the imperial insignia at a much later time; while the intertwining of dragons decorating the second *pi* is more akin to the dragon scroll of the second century BC than to corresponding earlier schemes (see numbers 143–148).

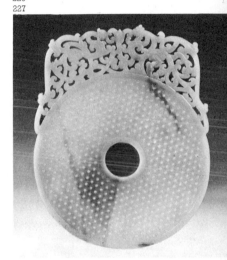

226
227

228

Pottery buildings of a farmstead excavated in 1951 at Cheng-chou, Honan.

Maximum height 76 cm, diameter of façade 93 cm
Eastern Han dynasty: 1st century AD

The custom of placing pottery models of buildings in tombs began in the first century AD. The roofs are tiled by the method invented four hundred years earlier (see numbers 132–134). Great buildings were built of timber, but the cost of this material put it beyond the reach of the majority in north China. Plain brick and stucco walls topped by roofs copied from the timber trabeate style were the rule for ordinary buildings in town and country. Some farmsteads are shown within a single wall like a defended place. Even when the wall is absent the back walls of the houses are usually without doors or windows.

228

229–234

Pottery figures of two acrobats and four musicians excavated in 1965 at Loyang.

Height 15 cm to 15.5 cm
Eastern Han dynasty: 1st or 2nd century AD

Entertainers came to China from Central Asia after the expansion of Chinese power through the Tarim basin under the emperor Wu Ti at the end of the second century BC. Jugglers and acrobats were popular in the Han period, and later musicians introduced the Indian music which had entered the Central Asian states, especially Kuča, with Buddhism. The instruments played by two of the musicians of the exhibit are probably *yüeh*, resembling Pan pipes; another sings and the fourth is blowing into his hands, which perhaps hold a small ocarina.

229–234

(DW)

8

Three Kingdoms
AD 220-65

Western Chin dynasty
AD 265-316

Eastern Chin dynasty
AD 317-420

Northern and Southern
dynasties (Wei, Chou, Ch'i, Sung
Liang)
AD 420-580

六朝

Period of the Six dynasties
AD 220-580

One eventual result of the communications with the far west opened by the Emperor Wu Ti's campaigns at the end of the second century BC was the entry of the Buddhist religion into China. The first knowledge of it penetrated in the second century AD, but the founding of temples and carving of images of Buddha and Bodhisattvas begins in the fourth and fifth centuries. Under the Northern Wei dynasty (AD 319-535) cave temples were cut in cliffs at Yün-kang in Shansi and Lung-men near the now dynastic capital at Loyang. Contrasting sculptural styles are seen at these two places. At Yün-kang work was executed under Central Asian influence, in which elements of the Greco-Bactrian art of north-west India are preserved; while at Lung-men, from AD 500, Chinese taste asserts itself, with emphasis on linear schemes and geometrically analysed form rather than on the organic unity of figures. Like some other arts in the disrupted national life of this period, the history of sculpture follows an erratic course, responding to successive but not closely related influence from Buddhist centres outside China, and to the effect of intermittently improved political relations at home. Gradually certain ateliers became established for the production of Buddhist sculpture, irrespective of local connexion with temples. One of the best documented of these was at Ting-chou in Hopei, where a metamorphosed limestone was particularly suitable and attractive. Work continued here from the early fifth century until the T'ang period, the subjects treated reflecting both the Hinayanist and the initial Mahayanist phases of Chinese

Buddhism. During the Six dynasties Chinese political control of Central Asia and the routes to the west was temporarily lost, but Buddhist pilgrims, of whom Fa Hsien is the best known, still passed to and from India.

The development of ceramics during this period makes a fascinating study. For inexplicable reasons the use of lead glaze on pottery was temporarily abandoned, although it must have continued in use for roof tiles. The production of high-fired ware with feldspathic glaze was concentrated in the south of Kiangsu and the north of Chekiang, in the region of the ancient kingdom of Yüeh, where work in colour of glaze and refinement of body and shape was at all times superior to that of other kilns in the south. From the beginning of the fifth century, in the period of the Northern and Southern dynasties (i.e. the later part of the Period of Six dynasties) China was divided politically north and south, along a line separating the great river valleys, to a degree reflected in the arts, even in ceramics. Yüeh ware continued on its course of gradual improvement, while radical experiment was confined to the north. Certain tall vases imitating a Central Asian style reminiscent of Iranian art were made in the north with feldspathic glaze. One such piece is dated to AD 565 and is quite un-Chinese in design, imitating the repoussé ornament of silverware of a provincial east Iranian kind. Before the end of the Six dynasties a revived interest in lead-glazing appears, heralding the elaborate and massive production of soft-glazed wares in Shensi during the first half of the T'ang dynasty.

244,245

243

235-239

289

241

235 (DW)

236

237

235

Green-glazed stoneware vase crowned with human figures and buildings in two tiers, proto-*Yüeh* ware, excavated in 1965 at Shao-hsing, Chekiang.

Height 46.6 cm
Western Chin dynasty AD 265–316

The custom of portraying groups of immortals or Taoist deities took root in popular art in the Shao-hsing district near modern Hankow. On bronze mirrors made here in the second century AD appear the portraits of the Queen Mother of the West and of the King Duke of the East, with their winged servitors. The identity of other genies accompanying them or depicted alone is less certain. About a century later a similar theme is taken up by the potter, but with no differentiation of the immortals. The buildings modelled on this vase are probably intended as their paradise in the western mountains.

236

Green-glazed stoneware jar decorated with a bird's head, proto-*Yüeh* ware, excavated in 1964 at Nanking, Kiangsu.

Height 17 cm
Western Chin dynasty : AD 265–316

In the third century the grey fabric of proto-*Yüeh* stoneware admits some impurities, the thin glaze tending to oxidize in patches to a yellowish tone. The improvement of the glaze colour by more complete control of the kiln atmosphere was the potter's great aim. In this piece a satisfactorily uniform colour has been achieved.

237

Green-glazed stoneware vessel shaped like a lion, proto-*Yüeh* ware, found in 1966 at Tan-yang, Kiangsu.

Height 17.5 cm
Western Chin dynasty : AD 265–316

Lion-shaped pots as water-holders for the scholar's desk, or urinals, were a popular product of the Chekiang and Kiangsu kilns.

238

Green-glazed stoneware ewer proto-*Yüeh* ware, excavated in 1967 at Yü-yao, Chekiang.

Height 23.5 cm
Eastern Chin dynasty : AD 317–419

Ewers decorated with a bird's head (it is not a spout) have a long history in proto-*Yüeh* ceramics, from the first attainment of tolerably clear green glaze shortly after AD300 until the opening of the T'ang dynasty, when the idea was retained and copied elsewhere, but in different designs. Flaws in the glaze caused by kiln contacts or contamination are still common. Brown-spotted green ewers and black ewers were also made.

238

239

Green-glazed stoneware vase with dished mouth and eight ring handles *Yüeh* ware, excavated in 1964 at Jui-an, Chekiang.

Height 26 cm
Period of the Southern dynasties: middle or late 5th century AD

An evolution of the vase shape from subspherical to taller proportions, with a cyma profile, may be followed through the fourth and fifth centuries. The dish-shaped mouth is a peculiarity of pre-T'ang potting in the Yüeh region.

240

Green-glazed stoneware jar with incised ornament and eight handles, excavated in 1958 at P'u-yang, Honan.

Height 29 cm
Northern Ch'i dynasty: AD 549–577

Potters in northern China did not emulate the stoneware of the Chekiang-Kiangsu region until the mid-sixth century, when they began to make tall vases with thick grey body and a glassy green or brown glaze, more fluid than the contemporary glaze of the south. The P'u-yang find typifies the northern products. The lower part of this vase remains white (unoxidized), testifying to kiln efficiency.

240
241

241

Green and brown-glazed jar decorated with petal-shaped lappets on the sides, excavated in 1958 at P'u-yang, Honan.

Height 23.5 cm
Northern Ch'i dynasty: AD 549–577

The brown-striped green glaze appears to be fluxed with lead and low-fired. Little is known of the history of lead glaze after its brief flowering in the Han period until its reappearance towards the middle of the sixth century. This jar is one of the earliest of the later phase, its variegation anticipating the development of three-colour lead glazes in T'ang.

239

242

242

Brown-glazed earthenware flask *pien hu,* decorated with moulded figures, excavated in 1971 from the tomb of the Generalissimo Fan Ts'ui at Anyang, Honan.

Height 20.3 cm
Northern Ch'i dynasty: AD 575

The so-called pilgrim's flask, which copies a leather bottle, was introduced to the Chinese potter from Central Asia, and is regularly decorated with exotic Western Asian themes. On this flask a man standing on a lotus-shaped pedestal is dancing to music provided by players on lute, cymbals and flute, and a singer. The beading around the neck and the palmette and half-palmettes on the shoulder are also borrowed from western Central Asia. The glaze is lead-fluxed and low-

fired, reintroducing this technique after long neglect in China (compare number 241).

243

Stele of white marble representing the Buddha Śākyamuni seated under śala trees between disciples and Bodhisattvas, excavated in 1959 at Lin-chang, Hopei.

Height 72.6 cm
Northern Ch'i dynasty: AD 549–577

The alabaster-like marble of Ting-chou in Hopei was used by a school of Buddhist sculptors from the early fifth century. Openwork in meticulous high relief in the glory above the figures is frequent in images carved in Hopei and Shantung during the following century. Śākyamuni's gestures show him as *abhayadāna*, bestower of fearlessness. At this period in China the iconography does not clearly distinguish his Bodhisattva companions, the outermost figures, who are Manjuśrī and Samatabhadra. The intervening figures are disciples, including Mahakasyapa, who became the leader of the disciples after the death of the Buddha, and Ananda, Śākyamuni's favourite. The trees forming the background are the twin *śala* in the grove in which Śākyamuni entered nirvana. Heavenly goddesses, *apsarases,* hold a garland of flowers over the Blessed One. On the base of the stele royal lions guard a censer.

244, 245

Stone sockets for wooden pillars carved with dragons in high relief, found in 1966 in the tomb of Ssŭ-ma Chin-lung at Shih-chia-chai, near Ta-t'ung, Shansi.

Height 16.5 cm, width 32 cm, and 32.6 cm
Northern Wei dynasty: AD 484

244

245

244A

245A

These stones are two of four found in the approach to the inner chamber of the three-chamber brick tomb and in the inner chamber itself, where they lay after disturbance by grave robbers. It is thought that they originally supported a screen placed on the east side of the inner chamber opposite the coffin dais occupying the west side. The stones were carved at the culmination of Northern Wei sculpture, as it is exemplified in monumental scale at the Buddhist cave-temples of Yün-kang near to the capital at Ta-t'ung. The lotus petals around the sockets and the formal leaf scrolls on the sides of the base are motifs of Buddhist art, introduced from western Asia, while the dragons pacing over hill-tops and sea are taken from the Chinese tradition. Three of the figures carved at the corners of one of the stones are musicians playing the small waist drum or *yao-ku*, the *pieh-li* trumpet of the west-China hillmen, and the *p'i-p'a* lute, while the fourth dances. Their treatment well illustrates the full rounded relief of the middle phase of Northern Wei style.

(CG)

9

新疆出土

Central Asia from the Han to the T'ang dynasty
1ST CENTURY BC – 8TH CENTURY AD

In 128 BC the Emperor Wu Ti sent Chang Ch'ien through Central Asia in the hope of securing the Yüeh-chih people as allies against the Hsiung-nu tribes who were harassing his north-western frontier. Some of the cultural results of this extraordinary mission, China's first deliberate contact with Western Asia, are described in the catalogue entries concerning horses and textiles. Chang Ch'ien's report, incorporated by Ssŭ-ma Ch'ien in his history, is our chief source of knowledge of the eastern part of the Iranian empire at this time. Besides news of horses and wine, Chang Ch'ien is credited with the introduction into China of many species of useful plants and fruit trees. Within a generation Parthia (Chinese P'o-ssŭ) and China were in diplomatic relations and a regular trade between them had begun. The first caravan is said to have gone through from the east in 106 BC. The routes to the north and south of the Tarim Basin – the 'Silk Route' – were in constant use even during the period of the Six dynasties when Chinese control of the oasis cities situated along them was relaxed. In the middle of the fifth century AD the Chinese state of Northern Wei sent armies into Central Asia, but it was not until the mid seventh century that Chinese authority was widely restored. The dry Central Asian soil has preserved fragments of the silk that was traded to the west. These give proof of the advanced technique of Chinese weaving and of the interchange of artistic ideas which the Silk Route facilitated. Missions were intermittenlty exchanged between China and the oasis cities and Sogdiana. Luxury goods of all kinds came to the Chinese court, particularly precious stones, medical materials, carpets. Servants and entertainers sought their fortunes in the east or were sent as tribute. The Sui emperors maintained a school of Central Asian music at their court. The end came in 638 with the Arab invasion of Iran. An appeal was addressed to the Chinese court by the last Sasanian ruler (or his son), but did not elicit Chinese intervention. In 670-3 Firuz, the son of Yezdegerd III of Iran, came himself to Ch'ang-an, the T'ang capital. A Persian trading community existed there, and was authorized to build its own temples.

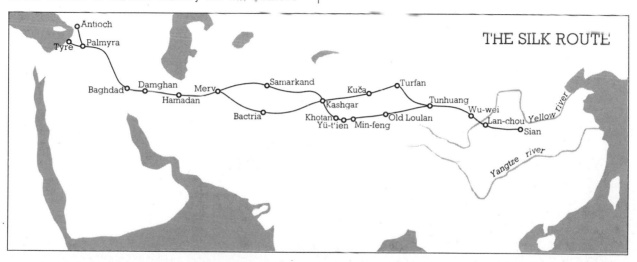

THE SILK ROUTE

246

249

250 (DW)

246

Mitten of five-coloured silk damask with woven inscription, excavated in 1959 at Min-feng (Niya), Sinkiang.

Length 24 cm
Eastern Han dynasty : 1st or 2nd century AD

Min-feng is the modern name of a post on the Southern Silk Route between Lou-lan and Khotan from which military colonies were administered after the Emperor Wu Ti's campaigns at the end of the second century BC. A large number of silks were found here in a grave. The pattern of the mitten implies 75 different selections of the warps. Its original red may have been darker ; the light blue, fawn and brown are well preserved. The sentence woven into the fabric reads :

May you extend your years, increase your longevity and be favoured with children and grandchildren.

The indeterminate design seems to represent animals among trees.

247, 248

Two fragments of a woollen damask with a vine in blue on a yellow ground, excavated in 1959 at Min-feng (Niya), Sinkiang.

Length 22.5 cm–26 cm
Eastern Han dynasty : 1st or 2nd century AD

This textile was recovered at a habitation site three kilometres southwest of the cemetery where the mitten number 246 was found. It is remarkable in composing the pattern with the wefts, a technique not followed in metropolitan China. Central Asians were exceedingly fond of wine, and even to the Chinese the acquisition of the vine seems to have rated second only to the celestial horses of Western Asia (see numbers 206 and 222 ff). The historian Ssŭ-ma Ch'ien ascribes the introduction of wine to China, about 100 BC, to the Chinese envoys. His successor Pan Ku believes that at first only a report of it came, but concludes that the reports concerning celestial horses and the grape led to the opening of communications with Ta-yüan (Bactria or Ferghana).

249

Fragment of a woollen band woven in four colours, excavated in 1959 at Min-feng (Niya), Sinkiang.

Length 29 cm
Eastern Han dynasty : 1st or 2nd century AD

250

Fragment of yellow silk twill with lozenge pattern, excavated in 1959 at Min-feng (Niya), Sinkiang.

Length 24.5 cm
Eastern Han dynasty : 1st or 2nd century AD

The density of the two pieces of Han twill found at Min-feng was 66 warp threads and 26–36 weft threads to the centimetre, which, given the average width of Han silk weave, implies more than 3,000 warps. The earliest silk twill known in China is that recorded in impressions made

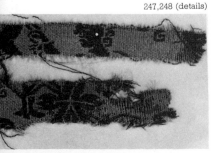

247,248 (details)

on the corroded surface of silk-wrapped bronzes buried in tombs of the Shang dynasty. In the Shang cloth no straight weave is visible among the floating threads; but in the twill of the Han period alternate warps are left to interweave normally between the twilled warps, so that some straight weave appears in the midst of the twill.

251

Fragment of five-coloured silk damask with stylized trees, excavated in 1959 at Astana, near Turfan, Sinkiang.

Length 20.5 cm
Period of the Northern dynasties: AD 551

From the Eastern Han, when it was the capital of the King of Chü-shih-ch'ien (a petty state protected by the Chinese), until the fourth century AD when it was taken into the Chinese dominion, Turfan increased in economic importance, and finally succeeded in attracting the bulk of the east-west trade from the Southern Silk Route to the Northern. The trees of this damask have an archaic appearance in Chinese terms, recalling a convention of the Han period rather than the freer vegetable designs of the Six dynasties. Red, blue, green, yellow and white was a favourite combination from Han times (compare number 246). The silk was found in grave 303 together with a burial tablet dated to AD 551.

Colour plate.

252

Woollen cloth dyed by wax-resist with yellow rosettes and rondels on a blue ground, excavated in 1959 at Yü-t'ien, Sinkiang.

Length 11 cm
Northern dynasties: early 5th century AD

Yü-t'ien is a small town in the south of the Tarim Basin which came under the jurisdiction of the city of Khotan from the late third century AD. The Buddhist pilgrim Hui-sheng passing there in AD 519 remarked on the coloured banners with their 'myriad devices' hanging in the temples of the town. These were probably of silk. Thin silk plain weave was the more usual material for wax-resist dyeing. Comparison with silks recovered at Turfan suggest a date for the Yü-t'ien fragment in the first decades of the fifth century.

253

Fragment of eight-colour silk damask with birds and flowers, excavated in 1968 at Astana, near Turfan, Sinkiang.

Length 38.2 cm
T'ang dynasty: AD 778

The double warps are 26 to the centimetre (52 in all). Of the eight coloured wefts only three are used in the design at any one place, so that 96 threads make up a density of 32 to the centimetre. The chief motif is a five-coloured posy, surrounded by other flowers, phoenixes and what appears to be the magic fungus,

251 (DW)

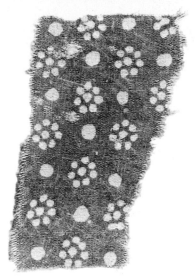

252

253 (detail)

ling-chih. The piece was found in grave 381, which also included a manuscript dated to AD 778. It represents one of the most elaborate of T'ang weaves. From about 650 to 750 Turfan, having been included in the T'ang dominion, greatly increased its population, becoming the largest city in Chinese territory west of Liang-chou in north Kansu.

254

Fragment of silk damask with confronted birds in beaded circles, excavated in 1969 at Astana, near Turfan, Sinkiang.

Length 26 cm
T'ang dynasty : early 8th century AD

For half a century and more after about AD 650 the damasks of Turfan surpassed all that had been achieved earlier. Sasanian Persia supplied the popular motif of real and imaginary animals set within oval or circular beaded panels, often paired in heraldic symmetry. The damask is generally worked in reverse twill, as here. This came from grave 138 in the T'ang dynasty cemetery.

255

Fragment of silk damask with wine-jar and two topers, excavated in 1969 at Astana, near Turfan, Sinkiang.

Length 12.8 cm
T'ang dynasty : 8th century AD

256

Fragment of yellow silk gauze with lighter-coloured ornament of birds and floral sprays dyed by wax-resist, excavated in 1968 at Astana, near Turfan, Sinkiang.

Length 57 cm
T'ang dynasty : AD 721

Gauzes were woven from the Han period onwards. Here the gauze is a straight weave with a density of 40 warps and 26 wefts to the centimetre. The wefts consist either of a single thread or a bundle of three, each used twice before changing to the other. The association of paired birds with flowers in a vase is copied from Sasanian Persia, but the birds in this case are very Chinese : Mandarin ducks. The piece came from grave number 108 together with a cloth document dated to AD 721.

257

Fragment of a paper manuscript of the Confucian Analects with the commentary by Cheng Hsüan, excavated in 1967 at Astana, near Turfan, Sinkiang.

Length 53 cm, height 28.5 cm
T'ang dynasty : AD 710

From grave 363 in the T'ang dynasty cemetery ; the date is written on the manuscript. The text of the fragment extends from the end of VII.11 to the beginning of VII.18, and contains two famous passages. As translated by Legge they are :

257 (DW)

'When the Master was in Ch'i he heard the *shao* (i.e the music of the Succession Dance) and for three months did not know the taste of meat' [see numbers 102–110];

The Master said 'With coarse rice to eat, with water to drink, and my bended arm for a pillow – I have still joy in the midst of these things. Riches and honours acquired by unrighteousness are to me as a floating cloud'.

258

Paper manuscript contract for a loan of money, signed by Po Huai-lu, excavated in 1964 at Astana, near Turfan, Sinkiang.

Height 29 cm
T'ang dynasty : 8th or 9th century AD

The names at the end are those of the lender, the borrower, a guarantor and two persons pledged as surety. In the event of default the creditor will recover on the debtor's property and on the persons of his household.

259–261

Food excavated in 1960 at Turfan, Sinkiang.

Length 18 cm, 5 cm, 6 cm
T'ang dynasty : 8th or 9th century AD

One piece is a roll of wheaten bread fried in oil, the other two are *chiao-tzǔ*, the still much appreciated Chinese ravioli.

258

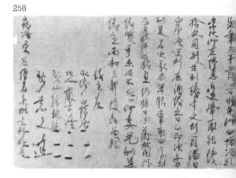

260,261

259

10

隋
唐

Sui dynasty
AD 581-618

T'ang dynasty
AD 618-906

The T'ang period is the classical age of Chinese civilization, an age of elegance, abundance, exuberant art, and unsurpassed achievement in verse and prose literature. The Sui dynasty is a prelude to it, during which roads and canals essential to the redistribution of grain and the maintenance of peace were constructed. A Grand Canal was dug to join the Yangtze to the Yellow river system, providing a navigable stretch of more than 1500 kilometres. A bridge built by the emperor Li Kung shortly before AD 600 is still standing, its arch spanning forty metres. The method of piercing the stone work above the arch with vaulted passages, to lighten the load of masonry and reduce the pressure of flood water against it, was a remarkable new achievement in engineering. The restoration of Chinese suzerainty over the small kingdoms of Central Asia boosted the manufacture and export of silks. Iranian influence is strong in textiles, pottery and silver ware.

Gradually the lead glaze of Sui became lighter in colour, and then a clear-glaze was produced,

The An-chi bridge of Sui dynasty date in Chao-hsien, Hopei.

giving a creamy surface to the clay figurines which were now increasingly placed in tombs (this practice had begun in Han and continued sporadically through the Six dynasties). To the clear lead glaze the T'ang potter added metal colorants to produce browns and yellows, green and blue. Full polychromy (conventionally called three-colour glazing, although a varying number of colours appear) was achieved between AD 700 and 710, the famous *T'ang san-ts'ai.* The first step in this process is represented by the flask number 242, covered with brown glaze and decorated in a wholly west-Asian style. The dates of tombs with three-colour pottery all fall in the first half of the eighth century AD. After the catastrophe of the rebellion of AD 756, three-colour pottery in the metal-derived shapes, so much favoured previously, was apparently no longer made, and there is less polychromy in lead glazes. During the heyday of 700-56 the polychrome glazes imitated dyed textiles, or reproduced formalised floral designs in which the colours were kept apart by grooves impressed in the surface of the clay. The glazes were generally applied over a slip of white clay. T'ang and three-colour ware was imitated both in Japan and in Mesopotamia. It may have reached Western Asia overland, or have been included in shipments made to the West from the Arab and Persian trading community established at Canton before AD 758.

Animal and human figurines were decorated with the same glazes. Not all the T'ang figurines were glazed, as a number of pieces in the exhibition show, but the finest sculpture of this kind generally took advantage of the brilliant fired colours. The total of figures consigned to a tomb of importance had grown to some hundreds by the end of the seventh century. They portray the favourite activities and the servants of the deceased, to show off his fine horses and his concern with the exotic trade coming from Central Asia by camel. A minority of the figures represent guardian genies, *pi-hsieh.* At a great funeral the figures were displayed outside the tomb as the cortège approached.

It is not until after AD 700 that the figures are of striking sculptural quality, which is a skilfully posed and modelled naturalism. This is seen no less in brawny foreign huntsmen caught in an energetic movement than in the haughty and plausibly vacuous beauties of the T'ang court. In compelling glance and gesture, the figures are superior to the Tanagra figures of Greece. The phase of Chinese art which they represent is isolated; the T'ang style could hardly be anticipated from the figurines of the previous century, and it has no sequel after the mid-eighth century. A like realism is found in a type of Buddhist guardians carved with exaggerated and approximately accurate anatomy, which also are confined to the T'ang period. The tomb figurines were moulded, but the best of them received further individual treatment before they were fired, in the modelling of details and the careful application of glaze. The unglazed pieces were painted in earth colours after firing.

Although many objects from rich T'ang tombs had reached museums, and the horse figurines in particular had become the best known of all Chinese antiquities, no large tomb of the period had been officially opened and systematically recorded before the excavation of the Princess Yung T'ai's mausoleum in 1964. According to the epitaph this girl of nineteen years died in childbirth, but the histories state that she was flogged to death, or made to hang herself, by order of her grandmother, empress Wu Tsê T'ien, who mistakenly took offence at a conversation reported to her. In 705, five years after Wu's death and when her father the

242

282,284,
287

273-2
281
299,3

A section drawing along the main axis of the tomb of the princess Yung T'ai, in Ch'ien-hsien, Shensi. T'ang dynasty.

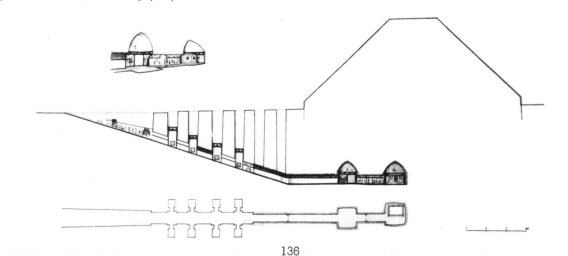

emperor had resumed the throne, Yung T'ai was accorded a sumptuous funeral, and united to the husband who had died with her. The excavators first removed earth from the vicinity of the tomb mound, which rises to a height of twelve metres in the shape of a truncated pyramid. Thus were revealed the tops of vertical shafts which had been sunk to facilitate the excavation of the sloping passage giving access from the surface to the funeral chamber, the latter being placed at a depth of twelve metres below the mound. One of the vertical shafts had been disturbed by a robbers' tunnel, and this was followed by the excavators into the interior of the tomb as a first step in clearing it. Where the tunnel reached the underground passage leading to the funeral chamber lay the skeleton of a man apparently killed by his fellow-robbers, perhaps an informant. A white tiger was painted on the west wall of the sloping entrance passage, and a green dragon on the east wall. On the walls of the antechamber were murals of Yung T'ai's attendants. In the chamber was a stone sarcophagus constructed of slabs about two metres high, engraved with floral designs. Other paintings and engravings adorned the passage walls, and in niches opening from the sloping entrance were placed solid ranks of pottery figurines, of which 777 are unglazed and painted, and some 60 glazed in the three-colour style: soldiers, servants, huntsmen, courtiers, horses, camels. Pottery and silver vessels were scattered along the passage where they had been abandoned by the thieves, who probably entered the tomb shortly after it was sealed.

The art of the T'ang goldsmith and silversmith is illustrated in the exhibition by pieces found in 1970 in Ho-chia, a suburb of the town of Sian. The latter is the modern equivalent of the T'ang capital, Ch'ang-an ('Long-lasting peace') whose site is close by. The treasure of precious metal was contained in two pottery jars and a silver vessel, amounting in all to more than a thousand pieces. It was excavated from the site of a mansion that belonged to a cousin of the emperor Hsüan Tsung, Li Hsiu-li, Prince of Pin who died in AD 741. It was perhaps buried when the emperor and the court had to leave Ch'ang-an at the outbreak of An Lu-shan's rebellion in 756. Among the silver were found coins of the Sasanian king Chosroes II (560-627), the Byzantine emperor Heraclius (610-41), and five Japanese coins struck in 708. With the single exception of a rhyton carved in onyx (not included in the exhibition) which is an import from Iran, or copies an Iranian piece, the treasure consists of Chinese work, in the decorative style peculiar to silver, in which shapes and ornament betray influence of Iranian silverwork but do not

reproduce it exactly. The cup number 306 is particularly close to its Sasanian prototype.

The exhibition includes an outstanding example of a white porcellaneous ware which was produced at Hsing-chou in Hopei, the finest ware produced by T'ang potters in high-fired ceramics.

306

288

272

,277

-275
278,
-281

-312

-328

137

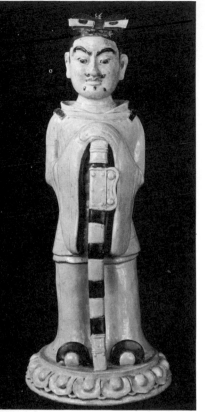

262 (DW)

264-271

262, 263

Figures of tomb guardians in stoneware with creamy white and dark brown glaze, excavated in 1959 from the tomb of General Chang Sheng at Anyang, Honan.

Height 71 cm, 64 cm
Sui dynasty : AD 595

The tradition of portraying military guardians of the tomb in approximately contemporary costume and armour continues from the Han dynasty. The ceramics in the tomb confirm the Sui date of the cream glaze and compared with figures of the Northern Wei period show greater realism in the modelling. The figures may have been made at kilns at Chia-pi-ts'un near to Anyang. The soldier with brown-glazed detail wears court costume. The other, in armour, has the leather helmet of the northerners and differs less from earlier figurines.

264–271

Eight stoneware figures of musical ladies covered with creamy white glaze, excavated in 1959 from the tomb of General Chang Sheng at Anyang, Honan.

Heights 17.2 cm–19 cm
Sui dynasty : AD 595

Figurines of musicians placed in tombs, rare since the Han dynasty (compare numbers 229–234), are now always female. The orchestra consists of two lute-players, a harpist and cymbalist, two flautists, a player of Pan pipes and a singer.

272

Attendants on the princess Yung T'ai, *hand-copied from*

263 (DW)

272

272

a coloured painting on the west wall of the antechamber of her tomb excavated in 1964 at Ch'ien-hsien, Shensi.

Length 440 cm
T'ang dynasty: AD 706

The young ladies carry domestic comforts: fan, back-scratcher, candle, cup, boxes containing probably com-fits and cosmetics, and bundles which may be silks. They are dressed in the prevailing Central Asian fashion of the time, with high waist and narrow sleeves, and a stole over the shoulders. On the extreme left is a girl (as is supposed) wearing male costume of corres-ponding style.

273-275

Painted pottery figures of horsemen from the tomb of the princess Yung T'ai, excavated in 1964 at Ch'ien-hsien, Shensi.

Height 32 cm, 30.5 cm, 31.5 cm
T'ang dynasty: AD 706

The modelling of the muscular horseman resembles the heroic naturalism adopted by Buddhist artists of the eighth century in painting and carving various spiritual guardians. The horsemen, bearded and big-nosed, are meant for Central Asians who were numerous in the Chinese capital and served in great houses. Their cos-tume with broad lapels, belt and baggy trousers follows the west Asian fashion. The man with an unruly cheetah is a huntsman, and the others are normal retainers. At least two of them have stirrups.

Colour plate.

276,277

Two ink impressions of female figures engraved on slabs of the outer stone coffin of the princess Yung T'ai, in the tomb excavated in 1964 at Ch'ien-hsien, Shensi.

Height 136 cm
T'ang dynasty: AD 706

The costumes and head-dresses are in the Central Asian fashion. The birds and floral sprays come from the well-established repertory of T'ang ornament.

278, 279

Pottery horses with green, yellow and brown glaze from the tomb of the princess Yung T'ai, excavated in 1964 at Ch'ien-hsien, Shensi.

Height 28 cm and 20.1 cm
T'ang dynasty: AD 706

These are in the tradition of the pottery and bronze figurines of the western horse made in the Han period (compare numbers 171, 172, 206, 222 ff) but are more natural than these or any of the pottery horses of the Six dynasties. The better observed realism which enters T'ang painting and sculpture in the late seventh century is reflected in the minor arts of the capital in the first half of the following century. Models and pictures of horses and equestrian portraits were in great demand.

273

276

275 (DW)

277

The style of Han Kan (active 752–756), the most famous of the horse painters, was influenced by the potter-sculptors. Not all admired the convention: Han Kan's contemporary, the poet Tu Fu, wrote:

Acclaimed from youth our Han Kan stands alone,
Exhausting every feature of the horse.
Alas – he paints the flesh and not the bone:
Such splendid beasts, but winded soon of course!

280, 281

Pottery figures of mounted huntsmen with green and brown glaze, from the tomb of the princess Yung T'ai, excavated in 1964 at Ch'ien-hsien, Shensi.

Height 32 cm, 31 cm
T'ang dynasty: AD 706

The hunt and polo playing, fashionable pastimes, were commemorated in figurines and the mural paintings of tombs. The riders are stirrupless, although at this time the use of the stirrup was already known (see number 275). A small cheetah sits on the horse's rump without a leash.

282–284

Two pottery bowls decorated with the three-colour glaze and **a green glazed bowl,** from the tomb of the princess Yung T'ai, excavated in 1964 at Ch'ien-hsien, Shensi.

Height 7.4 cm, 2.7 cm, 8 cm
T'ang dynasty: AD 706

The two three-colour bowls imitate shapes which were made also in silver. Their fluid glazes produce the effect of knot-dyeing and wax-resist dyeing on silk.

285

Pottery horse with three-colour glaze from the tomb of the prince Yi Tê, excavated in 1972 at Ch'ien-hsien, Shensi.

Height 80 cm
T'ang dynasty: AD 701

Yi Tê, personal name Li Ch'ung-jun, the eldest son of the T'ang emperor Chung Tsung, died at the age of nineteen, a few years before his father's accession. His tomb is on the same scale, and was as splendidly furnished as that of the princess Yung T'ai (numbers 278 ff). This horse, restored from large fragments, is the largest and finest piece of the pottery retinue placed in the grave, and belongs with the best half-dozen works of this kind that survive. The ornaments of the harness are in Iranian taste.

286

Pottery bird-head ewer with three colour-glaze, excavated in 1961 at Loyang, Honan.

Height 32.2 cm
T'ang dynasty: first half of the 8th century AD

The bird-head ewer has a long history in Chekiang and Kiangsu (compare number 236). In its T'ang form,

278
279
280
274 (DW)
281

282
283
284
285

joining the polychrome lead-glazed ware made near the capital, it shares in the exotic ornament of the middle T'ang. Here, between formal flower sprays, a horseman whose mount is shown in the 'flying gallop' (see note on number 222), is delivering a Parthian shot.

287

Subspherical pottery vase with splayed foot and lid, covered with three-colour glaze, excavated in 1958 at Loyang, Honan

Height 21 cm
T'ang dynasty : first half of the 8th century AD

Colour plate.

288

White glazed porcellaneous spittoon excavated in 1955 at Sian, Shensi.

Height 10.5 cm
T'ang dynasty : second half of the 9th century AD

During the T'ang dynasty the first high-fired pottery attempted in north China was made in Honan (compare numbers 240 and 241) in imitation of the Kiangsu green-glazed stoneware of *Yüeh* tradition. Later a superlative porcellaneous white ware appears in the north. It is attributed to kilns recorded at Hsing-chou in Hopei, although the site of these has not been located. The piece exhibited represents the very highest quality achieved in this Hsing ware.

Colour plate.

286

287

289

White porcellaneous bowl on a high spreading foot, clear-glazed with applied medallions, excavated in 1956 at Han-sen-chai, near Sian, Shensi.

Height 23 cm
T'ang dynasty : AD 667

Applied decoration was a provincial west-Iranian style, seen on pottery at Khotan and other places. Hard-glazed ware with this kind of ornament was made in north China sporadically for about a century from the middle of the sixth century. This piece must stand at the beginning of the whiteware tradition represented by number 288. The tomb in which it was found, dated by a funerary tablet to AD 667, contained a pottery model of a western-barbarian head in Scythian cap, and a jar related to numbers 240 and 241.

Colour plate.

290

Stoneware jug with light and dark brown glaze, decorated with applied panels of bird, lion and floral medallion, excavated in 1958 on a kiln site at Wa-ni-tuan near Ch'ang-sha, Hunan.

Height 22.5 cm

288 (DW)

289 (DW)

290

T'ang dynasty: 9th century AD

The medallion and the lion include in the design the character *chang*, which is probably the potter's surname.

291

Brown glazed pottery figure of a bull excavated in 1965 at Ch'in-an, Kansu.

Length 46 cm
T'ang dynasty: first half of the 8th century AD

292

Camels and horsemen hand-copied from a coloured wall painting in the tomb of the heir-apparent prince Chang Huai (Li Hsien), investigated in 1971 at Ch'ien-hsien, Shensi.

Length 204 cm
T'ang dynasty: soon after AD 684

The paintings in the tomb depict the prince's amusements. Judging by the clubs carried by some of the horsemen the object here is a game of polo, and the camels carry the picnic. (See number 304.)

293–296

Pottery camel and horse with their attendants covered with three-colour glaze, excavated in 1959 from a tomb at Ch'ung-p'u, near Sian, Shensi.

Height 47.5 cm, 29.7 cm
T'ang dynasty: early 8th century AD

A fancifully loaded camel betokens wealth, if not actual involvement in the Central Asian trade. The boards projecting back and front are part of the pack saddle, the face of a hairy Central Asian an improbable ornament, and the load is vegetables and game. Despite the rich contents of this tomb, no inscription with the occupant's name and title was included in it.

297, 298

Pottery figures of tomb guardians covered with three-coloured glaze, excavated in 1959 from a tomb at Ch'ung-p'u, near Sian, Shensi.

Height 65.5 cm, 57.5 cm
T'ang dynasty: early 8th century AD

The figure dressed in armour, trampling on a demon and phoenix-crested, is a T'ang transformation of the ancient genie Fang-hsiang, whose occupation was to frighten away sickness and evil spirits. In the Han period pottery figures of Fang-hsiang were placed in graves, sometimes one in each corner, the question whether they protected the dead or the living being left unanswered. Through the Six dynasties the idea of four Fang-hsiang seems to have been assimilated in popular belief to the Buddhist concept of Four Heavenly Kings, whose duty it

292 (detail)

293,294

295,296

291

was to guard the four quarters of Heaven and to protect the state. The figure in armour is such a celestial guardian in angry aspect. Meanwhile another apotropaeic genie, Ch'i-t'ou, originally only a mask worn in the devil-clearing ceremony at the New Year, took on a new guise and assumed the function of the earlier Fang-hsiang. He is depicted horned, with large ears, flaming shoulders and a repellent visage. The *Feng su t'ung*, a Han work on popular beliefs, says of the Ch'i-t'ou:

> There is a vulgar superstition that the spirits of the dead roam abroad. Therefore the Ch'i-t'ou is made in order to keep them in one place. It is so called from its having an ugly big head. A name for it in another dialect is Ch'u-k'uang ('he who abuts on the grave').

As in this instance, two guardians in armour and two Ch'i-t'ou form a group placed in the burial chamber, one at each corner.

297 (CG)

298 (CG)

299, 300

Two pottery figures of ladies with three-colour glaze, excavated in 1959 from a tomb at Ch'ung-p'u, near Sian, Shensi.

Height 42 cm, 45 cm
T'ang dynasty: early 8th century AD

Orange-coloured beauty-spots, sometimes rosettes (as in number 300), are a Turfan fashion adopted at the Chinese capital. All over Central Asia and in China from the late seventh century women's dress favoured long pleated skirts, round necks, narrow sleeves and a stole. The coiffure with single top-knot is also exotic. In the opening decades of the eighth century women exposed the face and neck when they went out riding, and adopted the hats of their Central Asian maids instead of the old *wei-mao*, which combined a hat with an ample head shawl.

301

Bronze mirror decorated with a hunting scene, excavated in 1961 at Fu-kou, Honan.

Diameter 29 cm
T'ang dynasty: 8th or 9th century AD

The landscape of formal mountains and trees is arranged around the central knob, huntsmen with their steeds at the 'flying gallop' chase hare, boar, deer and monkey (see comment on number 138).

302

Bronze mirror with twin phoenixes, excavated in 1952 at Hsien-yang, Shensi.

Diameter 23 cm
T'ang dynasty: 8th or 9th century AD

Phoenixes are specially frequent in the decoration of mirrors. The male *feng* may appear alone, or paired with the female, *feng-huang*, as bringer of good fortune. Here the design is completed with parrots, lotus and scrolling stems. Birds and flower sprays alternate in the lobes of the lip.

299

300

301

302

303

304 (detail)

303

Bronze mirror with monsters and birds, excavated in 1955 at Sian, Shensi.

Diameter 21.5 cm
T'ang dynasty : 8th or 9th century AD

The theme of large-headed unidentified animals disporting themselves in a grape-vine is frequent as a decoration of mirror backs. The metaphor, no doubt bibulous, has not been solved.

304

Horsemen setting out at the gallop for the hunt, hand-copied from a coloured wall painting in the tomb of the heir-apparent Prince Chang Huai (Li Hsien), investigated in 1971 at Ch'ien-hsien, Shensi.

Length 240 cm
T'ang dynasty : soon after AD 684

Hunting from the saddle was conducted with the aid of cheetah, hawks, and Central Asian grooms and retainers who are distinguishable here by their turban-like hats. (See number 292).

305

Gold pedestal bowl with repoussé petals forming the sides, and traced ornament of deer, birds and flowers, excavated in 1970 at Ho-chia, Sian, Shensi

Height 5.5 cm, diameter 13.5 cm
T'ang dynasty : mid 8th century AD

The animals and the petals are of Chinese tradition, while the beading of the foot-rim and the scatter of flowers and leaves on a uniform ground are elements of Iranian style. The symmetrically flowering branches within the lower petals continue the leaf scrolls of the Six dynasties (compare numbers 244 and 246) in a freer idiom.

Colour plate.

305 (DW)

306

Silver-gilt cup on a pedestal, the sides in eight facets each framing a human figure, excavated in 1970 at Ho-chia, Sian, Shensi

Height 6.5 cm
T'ang dynasty : mid 8th century AD

The Iranian silver known in Central Asia and eventually in China appears to have been made mostly in Sogdiana, on the eastern edge of the Sasanian empire. This Chinese cup imitates the style in the beaded foot-rim (compare number 305) and the general shape, and in particular copies the Iranian handle, even to the point of decorating the upper surface of the handle escutcheon with the heads of two old men, in place of the royal or noble head which appears on Iranian pieces. The figures on the side hold musical instruments or cups, standing against a ground of the floral scrolling fashionable in the Chinese capital in the early eighth century.

306 (DW)

307

307A

308

309 (CG)

310

311

307

Round silver box with traced ornament of formal flowers and birds, excavated in 1970 at Ho-chia, Sian, Shensi.

Height 6 cm, diameter 13.5 cm
T'ang dynasty : mid 8th century AD

Radial designs of flowers reduced to a formal convention and interspersed with small flying birds are characteristic of one of the schools of silversmiths practising at the T'ang capital Ch'ang-an (Sian). This style contrasts with the freer treatment seen in number 308. Being found in the same hoard of silver the styles would appear to be roughly contemporary. It was previously thought that silver with comparatively realistic ornament, the product of another school, was later than that decorated in the formal manner.

308

Parcel-gilt bowl with traced peony scrolls inside and outside, excavated in 1970 at Ho-chia, Sian, Shensi.

Height 3 cm, diameter 10.1 cm
T'ang dynasty : mid 8th century AD

Peony fancying was popular in the eighth-century T'ang capital at Ch'ang-an (i.e. Sian). On the twentieth day of the third month when the flowers opened 'the whole town went mad'. Peonies are a constant ornament on silver, introducing a broad, free style (contrast number 307).

309

Winged cup *yü shang*, of parcel-gilt silver, decorated with traced peony scrolls inside and outside, excavated in 1970 at Ho-chia, Sian, Shensi.

Height 2.8 cm, longer axis 10.5 cm
T'ang dynasty : mid 8th century AD

The winged cup was popular in the Han period, when it was principally made of lacquered wood. In the T'ang dynasty it reappears in silver as an antiquarian revival, an ancient Chinese vessel to stand alongside others which copied Iranian shapes.

310

Parcel-gilt silver bowl and cover decorated with peony sprays, excavated in 1970 at Ho-chia, Sian, Shensi.

Height 11.4 cm, diameter 21.9 cm
T'ang dynasty : mid 8th century AD

This bowl was intended for serving rice. Its shape, with the lid, was imitated later in porcelain. Ornament arranged in separate panels in this manner is found on a category of silver ware, consisting mostly of large bowls, which may represent the work of a distinct atelier at Ch'ang-an.

311

Parcel-gilt silver bowl with a spout, excavated in 1970 at Ho-chia, Sian, Shensi.

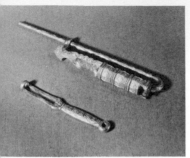

320,321

(Not on exhibition) 312

322,323

313 (CG)

Height 8.3 cm
T'ang dynasty : mid 8th century AD

This vessel was probably intended for ablution, like the Western Chou *yi*, and recalls the antiquarianism of the cup number 309.

312

Silver-gilt padlock excavated in 1970 at Ho-chia, Sian, Shensi.

Length 13.7 cm
T'ang dynasty : mid 8th century AD

The smaller piece is the key. This barrel or barb-bolt padlock was known also to the Romans, and has been found on Romano-British sites. A spring like the barbs of an arrow is attached to each side of the bolt, which after being inserted in the barrel cannot be removed until the springs are pressed against the stem by means of the ring at the end of the key. The principle of this lock was employed elsewhere in Asia ; it is not known where it was invented. Not on exhibition.

313

Silver coin of the Sasanian king Chosroes II, from excavations at Turfan in 1967.

Diameter 2.9 cm
7th century AD

Iranian coins found in Central Asia and on Chinese territory, particularly near Sian, betoken the trade passing along the Silk Route. This coin is similar to two that were found with the treasure of silver at Ho-chia (numbers 305–312, 314–328).

324,325

326,327
328

314–327

Two silver boxes and two lids, and four silver dishes containing cinnabar, jade, stalactite, amber, clear quartz and blue quartz, excavated in 1970 at Ho-chia, Sian, Shensi

Diameter of boxes and trays 17 cm, 17 cm, 14.4 cm, 14.3 cm, 18.1 cm, 18.7 cm
T'ang dynasty : mid 8th century AD

The inscription on the lid of the box with cinnabar and jade speaks of sets of white jade, 'deep marked' jade, 'bright fine red sand' (i.e. cinnabar), and *chüeh* (penannular rings). On the lid of the box with stalactite is written 'second quality stalactite 14 *liang* 3 *fen*. Can be taken medicinally'.

328

Silver bottle of pomegranate shape, excavated in 1970 at Ho-chia, Sian, Shensi.

Height 8.9 cm
T'ang dynasty : mid 8th century AD

314-317

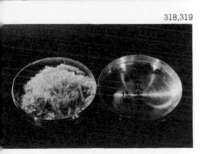

318,319

The last two sections of the exhibition contain almost exclusively porcelains through which a changing aesthetic and technical advance can be discerned. The course of Chinese art, as of politics and the national fortunes, runs comparatively smoothly, experiencing none of the revolutionary changes which occur in the evolution from Han to the end of T'ang. The period from the tenth to the fourteenth century spans the great age of Chinese painting, and any view of the cultural achievement which omits this branch of art is necessarily quite incomplete. In Sung painting, landscape was established as the most expressive and exacting category, displacing portraiture which had held this position earlier. With landscape painting went poetical contemplation, a philosophy of union with nature which often found its language in the literature of the Tao, while its sentiment could equally draw near to Buddhist quietism. The theorist tended to see finished paintings as the exteriorisation of an idea essentially subjective and barely communicable, a symbol of the working of *ch'i*, the underlying and harmonising spirit which animates and directs existence. At the same time the painter was held as never before to a discipline of formal training. He practised the drawing of all the objects he wished to represent until he could set them down without reflexion in composing a picture. The vocabulary of forms was limited, seldom going outside the limits of trees, rocks, flowers, abbreviated buildings and stereotyped human figures, although in each category many varieties must be clearly distinguished. The landscape was nearly always dominated by a towering and distant mountain and the viewer of the painting was invited to enter into it and to follow an indicated path into solitude and communion with nature. The ink, watercolour and silk or paper which provided the materials of painting were calculated to aid the rapidity and spontaneity of the artist's work, and

the question of its durability came second. To the landscape other well defined categories were added, such as birds and flowers, human figures, architecture. In the Sung period similar aesthetic claims came to be made of all of these, the craftsman being continually pressed towards philosophic depth.

The development of Sung painting and of the criticism of art which went with it depended on enlightened patronage. The greatest of all patrons was the emperor Hui Tsung, the last ruler of the Northern Sung period, whose reign was brought to an abrupt end when the Chin occupied the whole of north China. Through his Academy Hui Tsung presided over an important change in the tenor of the painting. The style of the Five dynasties and Northern Sung had been characterized by strong drawing and large clearly structured compositions, depicting a nature which could overawe as well as restore the mind. This was the style established by such masters as Ching Hao and Chü Jan. About the beginning of the twelfth century a more intimate approach is taken to the natural scene, and one is prepared for the closer views and the comforting atmosphere, not to say sentimentality, which give the dominant tone of painting in the Southern Sung period, ideally represented in the work of Ma Yuan.

In ceramic art a contrast is felt between the wares of northern tradition and those of South China, in which the latter, produced at their best under the patronage of the court, reflect a distinct aesthetic. The northern *Ting*, celadon and *Tz'ŭ Chou* porcelains favour bold floral decoration carved or painted, applied to traditional potter's shapes; the wares of the southern imperial kilns maximize the appeal of subtle glaze and delicate profile, and by the imitation of archaic bronze forms address themselves to the patron of cultivated taste and neo-Confucian sentiment.

338-344

333-336

(DW)

329

Tall necked stoneware vase with double ring handles, covered with green-brown glaze and decorated with floral designs in darker brown, *Yüeh* ware, excavated in 1969 at Lin-an, Chekiang

Height 50.7 cm
Five dynasties : AD 907–960

The design has been drawn in pigment containing more iron oxide than the glaze. The piece is no doubt a product of the Chekiang kilns of *Yüeh* tradition, which were soon to lose their primacy in celadons to the kilns of Lung-ch'uan at the southern end of the province.

330–332

Green-glazed deep bowl; jar with lid and basin with ring-handles, *Yüeh* ware, excavated in 1969 at Lin-an, Chekiang.

Height 9.5 cm, 19.6 cm, 9.2 cm
Five dynasties : AD 907–960

The smooth glaze and precise potting of the latest phase of the celadon tradition of *Yüeh* are second only to the Lung-ch'uan celadon of the Southern Sung period. The product of the north Chekiang potters never loses its unsophisticated air.

333

Celadon dragon jar with a dragon in high relief encircling the shoulder, excavated in 1956 at Lung-ch'üan, Chekiang.

Height 19 cm
Sung dynasty : 12th or 13th century AD

It is not known exactly when the activity of the kilns at Lung-ch'üan in south Chekiang began; it cannot have been before the eleventh century, and the best work was being done during the Southern Sung period, in the later twelfth or thirteenth centuries. The glazes are accomplished beyond anything achieved earlier at the *Yüeh* kilns.

334

Celadon bowl with inturned lip, the sides carved with petals, excavated in 1960 at Lung-ch'üan, Chekiang.

Height 6.5 cm, diameter 13.5 cm
Sung dynasty : 12th or 13th century AD

This is a near Eastern form, based on a Seljuq metal type.

335

Celadon water-dropper in the shape of a boat, excavated in 1956 at Lung-ch'üan, Chekiang.

Length 17.3 cm
Sung dynasty : 12th or 13th century AD

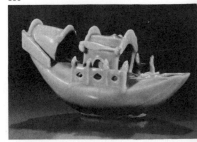

336 (DW)

338

336

Celadon tripod vessel *ting,* excavated in 1954 at Jui-an, Chekiang.

Height 12.4 cm
Sung dynasty : 12th or 13th century AD

The quality is the finest of the Lung-ch'üan ware. Under palace influence the kilns of the Southern Sung period produced ceramic versions of bronze vessels of the ancient ritual lineage, responding to the revived interest in Confucianism and its antiquarian lore.

337

Celadon tripod vessel *ting,* excavated in 1960 at Lan-t'ien, Shensi.

Height 27 cm
Sung dynasty : 12th century AD

The kilns at Yao-hsien in Shensi, of which this piece is an outstanding product, originated the tradition of 'northern' celadon ware. In the Sung period the archaising tendency noted at number 336 is more rarely seen in north China than in the south. This piece in the style of the later southern celadons copies a bronze vessel which is a much altered version of the ancient *ting,* the relief panels on the sides barely recalling the *t'ao-t'ieh* mask from which they derive through a series of distortions in book illustration.

Colour plate.

339

340

337 (DW)

338

Stoneware pillow with a picture of a boy fishing, Tz'ŭ-chou ware, excavated in 1955 at Hsing-t'ai, Hopei.

Length 28.8 cm
Sung dynasty : 12th century AD

339

White glazed porcelain ewer of the Buddhist shape, carved with lotus petals and floral scroll, *Ting* ware, excavated at Ting-hsien, Hopei.

Height 60.5 cm
Sung dynasty : 11th century AD

The 'pure water vase' is an appurtenance of the Buddhist altar. This piece is possibly the finest tall *Ting* vase that has ever been seen. Among other shapes, the *Ting* kilns of Hopei continued to produce some T'ang types, to which belong metal ewers resembling this piece.
This piece and the six following were found in the treasure buried, as the custom is, beneath a pagoda whose foundation was excavated at Ting-hsien.

340

Bowl of white glazed porcelain with the sides carved as petals, *Ting* ware, excavated in 1969 at Ting-hsien, Hopei.

Height 7.3 cm, diameter 21.9 cm
Sung dynasty : 11th century AD

See number 339.

341

342

341

White glazed porcelain model of a conch, *Ting* ware, excavated in 1969 at Ting-hsien, Hopei.

Length 19.8 cm
Sung dynasty : 11th century AD

This was made as a Buddhist symbol, since a conch trumpet is used in the religious service to sound the sacred syllable *om*. See number 339.

342

Five-legged white glazed porcelain censer, *Ting* ware, with five mask-topped legs attached to a foot-ring, excavated in 1969 at Ting-hsien, Hopei.

Height 24.1 cm
Sung dynasty : 11th century AD

See number 339.

343

White glazed porcelain saucer marked *kuan* (official), with lobed lip, *Ting* ware, excavated in 1969 at Ting-hsien, Hopei.

Height 3 cm, diameter 12.8 cm
Sung dynasty : 10th century

The claim to be 'official' is more frequently made of wares of the later Sung period, and is rarely seen on *Ting* porcelain. There is a tradition recorded in most later Chinese records that *Ting* ware enjoyed imperial patronage, as did the *mi-sê* (secret colour) *Yüeh* ware of Chekiang or the *Ju* ware of the north. On the back of the saucer is written in ink :

> Second year of the period T'ai-p'ing hsing-kuo [i.e. AD 977] fifth month twenty-second day : dedicated by the male believer Wu Ch'eng-hsün, who also dedicated in money thirty *wen*, sufficient for prayer to comfort the soul of his father.

See number 339.

343

344

White glazed spherical porcelain bottle with tall neck and a silver lid, the sides carved with lotus petals, *Ting* ware, excavated at Ting-hsien, Hopei

Height 19.8 cm
Sung dynasty : 11th century AD

See number 339.

344

345 (DW)

345

Porcelain ewer and bowl for warming wine, glazed light-blue, *ch'ing-pai* ware, excavated in 1963 at Su-sung, Anhui.

Height of ewer 25.8 cm, of the bowl, 14 cm
Sung dynasty : 12th or 13th century AD

346

Bowl with constricted neck and everted lip, glazed light blue, *ch'ing-pai* ware, excavated in 1965 at Tê-an, Kiangsi.

Height 9.8 cm, diameter 21.2 cm
Sung dynasty : 12th or 13th century AD

346

347

Bowl with incised floral design inside, glazed light blue, *ch'ing-pai* ware, excavated at Nan-ch'ang, Kiangsi.

Height 7.2 cm, diameter 20.5 cm
Sung dynasty : 12th or 13th century AD

Incised decoration, so characteristic of northern wares during the Sung period, appears in the south chiefly on *ch'ing-pai*. This ware enjoyed very wide patronage, being found distributed over north China and in Korea.

347

(CG)

Liao dynasty
AD 916-1125

Chin dynasty
AD 1115-1234

Yüan dynasty
AD 1271-1368

辽 金 元

The impact of the Mongol court upon the arts after 1271 is a debated question. Chinese writers make much of the opposition to the foreign rule expressed by painters who out of patriotism refused to serve at court. But it is difficult to assess what is owed to the sense of political frustration in the genesis of a new style in painting. This emphatically rejected the sentimental and by now stereotyped manner inherited from the Southern Sung Academy. It interpreted traditional subjects with new emphasis on expressive brushwork and on textural quality, in preference to explicit perspective and architectonic devices. Chao Meng-fu, who accepted the summons to the Yüan court, and Wang Meng who did not, and died in prison after his arrest for conspiracy, contributed equally to the success of the new movement.

In the minor arts the influence of an exotic taste introduced by the Yüan court is more apparent. In general it encouraged an exuberant space-filling decoration in negation of the Sung aesthetic, but the floral and other motifs employed were Chinese. The introduction of underglaze painting in blue in the fourteenth century was a signal event. The technique was copied from the Persian potters of Kashan, but improved to a degree which ensured control of the blue pigment sufficient for detailed brushwork in the designs. This was the beginning of the tradition of blue-and-white porcelain which was exported in large quantities, first to the Near East and from the sixteenth century to Europe, there eventually provoking many varieties of imitation in faience.

352-354
363

364,365
369,370

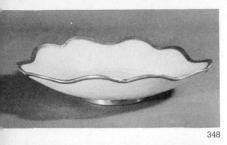

348

349

350,351

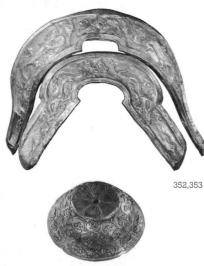

352,353

354

355

356-358

362

348

White porcelain dish inscribed *kuan* (official), excavated in 1953 at Ch'ih-feng, Liao-ning, from the tomb of the Prince of Wei.

Height 5.4 cm, diameter 22.3 cm
Liao dynasty : AD 959

349

White porcelain flask copying a leather bottle, excavated in 1953 at Ch'ih-feng, Liao-ning, from the tomb of the Prince of Wei.

Height 23.5 cm
Liao dynasty : AD 959

This shape is a favourite one in Liao ceramics, although it is not one found in the T'ang tradition which the Liao potters inherited.

350, 351

Two iron arrowheads with whistling barbs, excavated in 1953 at Ch'ih-feng, Liao-ning, from the tomb of the Prince of Wei.

Length 10 cm, 9.3 cm
Liao dynasty : AD 959

352–354

Silver-gilt saddle and harness ornaments excavated in 1953 at Ch'ih-feng, Liao-ning, from the tomb of the Prince of Wei.

Height 27.7 cm, 37.5 cm, 6 cm
Liao dynasty : AD 959

In the T'ang period silver had not been used so lavishly for the manufacture of utilitarian objects. Repoussé in high relief was a style favoured in the Mongol period, even for smaller ornaments.

355

Silver cup on a stand excavated in 1953 at Ch'ih-feng. Liao-ning, from the tomb of the Prince of Wei.

Height 8.5 cm, diameter of the tray 16 cm
Liao dynasty : AD 916–1125

356–358

Three pottery figures of actors in character from the façade of a tomb, excavated in 1969 at Hou-ma, Shansi.

Height 19.5–21 cm
Chin dynasty : AD 1115–1234

359–361

Three pottery figures of actors in character excavated in 1963 at Chiao-tso, Honan.

Height 37–39.2 cm
Yüan dynasty : AD 1271–1368

359 (CG)

360 (CG)

361 (CG)

362

Porcelain image of the Bodhisattva Kuan-yin (Avalokitesvara) covered with light blue glaze, *ch'ing-pai* ware, excavated in 1955 at the western end of the Ting-fu thoroughfare in the western sector of Peking.

Height 67 cm
Yüan dynasty : AD 1271–1368

Ceramic images of Buddhist deities are scarcely known before the Yüan period, when a series of fine works were produced in *ch'ing-pai* porcelain, distinguished by the delicacy of expression and the rich and exact ornament. The beaded lines of the latter are characteristic. In size and finish this piece surpasses any of the kind previously known. The manufacture of these figures appears to belong to the last decades of the thirteenth and the first decades of the fourteenth century.

363

Censer of coloured openwork earthenware with dragon and mountain over a tripod vessel, excavated in 1964 in the Hai-tien sector of Peking.

Height 36 cm
Yuan dynasty : AD 1271–1368

This piece is unmatched in Chinese work of earlier or later date. The rich and not archaistic decoration applied to an object which stands for Confucian traditionalism reflects a taste peculiar to the period. The censer was found in a disused well in the courtyard of the Yellow Temple outside the Tê-sheng gate. The ornament is built up of moulded elements in a technique not known after the Yüan period.

364

White porcelain vase and cover with underglaze decoration of leaf sprays and floral motifs in various panels, excavated in 1901 in the Hai-tien sector of Peking.

Height 55 cm
Yüan dynasty : late 14th century AD

This unparalleled vase was found outside the Tê-sheng gate. The purplish colour of the design suggests that copper is the basis of the underglaze pigment of the lid, while impure cobalt served elsewhere. The delicate floral design is more characteristic of the early Ming period, and this piece may have been made after 1368.

Colour plate.

365

White porcelain goblet *ku*, with underglaze blue decoration, excavated in 1962 at the entrance to Hsin-chieh in the western sector of Peking

Height 15.3 cm
Yüan dynasty : 14th century AD

The copying of the ancient ritual *ku* in a popular porcelain is a sign of the persistence in the Mongol period of the Confucian sentiment and artistic archaism which began under the Sung emperors.

363 (CG)

384 (DW)

365

366

Dish of purple glazed stoneware, *chün* ware, excavated in 1970 at Fang-shan, in Peking.

Height 5 cm, diameter 22.3 cm
Yüan dynasty: AD 1271–1368

This ware, known in purplish blue and green varieties, was produced at Yü-hsien and several other places in Honan, probably from the second quarter of the tenth century AD. It was made also in the early Ming period, probably at Ching-tê-chen in Kiangsi, and was imitated sporadically later.

366

367

367

Porcelain brush rest covered with light blue glaze, *ch'ing-pai* ware, excavated in 1962 in the western sector of Peking.

Length 18 cm
Yüan dynasty: AD 1271–1368

On the mountains of the rack grows the magic fungus, *ling-chih*.

368

Stoneware jar with design in black of two phoenixes, *Tz'ŭ-chou* ware, excavated from an underground storehouse at Liang-hsiang near Peking.

Height 36 cm
Yüan dynasty: AD 1271–1368

The painting is executed on a ground of white slip, the details incised through the black to the white beneath. The jar was found with thirty-four other pieces in a storehouse three metres below ground level.

369

Eight-faceted porcelain vase of *mei-p'ing* shape, with a lid, decorated in underglaze blue with dragons in waves, excavated in 1964 at Pao-ting, Hopei.

Height 51.5 cm
Yüan dynasty: 14th century AD

In a hoard of porcelain evidently buried by its owner for safety this vase accompanied three other blue-and-white pieces, equally distinguished, including the ewer number 370. Its shape and ornament are unique among the blue-and-white porcelains known from the fourteenth century. The combination of incised design (the bodies of the dragons) with painting in blue had not previously been observed.

Colour plate.

370

Porcelain ewer decorated with under-glaze blue, excavated in 1964 at Pao-ting, Hopei.

Height 26.5 cm
Yüan dynasty: 14th century AD

The ewer copies a Near Eastern metal prototype, a fashion frequent in Yüan ceramics, and among such ewers is unique in having faceted sides.

369 (DW)

368

370

371

Stoneware bowl with mottled blue and purple glaze, *chün* ware, excavated in 1964 at Pao-ting, Hopei.

Height 10.6 cm, diameter 44 cm
Yüan dynasty : AD 1271–1368

372

Round silver box with lobed edges, engraved with two phoenixes, excavated in 1955 at Ho-fei, Anhui.

Height 15.9 cm, diameter 35 cm
Yüan dynasty : AD 1271–1368

373

Round lacquer box carved with a scene of an old man under a pine tree beside water, attended by a boy, found in 1953 in one of a series of tombs of close date, belonging to the Jen family, which included that of the painter Jen Jen-fa (died 1327), at Ch'ing-p'u-hsien near Shanghai.

Height 3.9 cm, diameter 21.1 cm
Yüan dynasty : second quarter of the 14th century AD

374–385

Silver toilet box and its contents of eleven toilet instruments excavated in 1964 at Suchow, Kiangsu.

Height of the box 24.3 cm
Yüan dynasty : AD 1271–1368

371

374 385

372

373

古为今用

'Let the past serve the present'
MAO TSE-TUNG